# Pain-Free Childbirth

## Every Woman's Blessing In Jesus

Andrews, Nissa

PAIN-FREE CHILDBIRTH

/ Nissa Andrews – 1st ed.

ISBN 978-0-9983068-4-1

Printed in the United States of America

Design by DreamSurf Publishing

www.DreamSurfPublishing.com

FIRST EDITION

This book is dedicated to my daughter Glory. It contains everything I want to pass down to you regarding your future journey to motherhood, pregnancy, and childbirth.

Forever my love,

Mom

# Table of Contents

00  Introduction ................................................. 5

01  Humble Beginnings ................................. 8

02  The Great Exchange ............................... 20

03  Supernatural Pregnancy ........................ 34

04  My Pain-Free Birth Testimonies ........... 44

05  Who Will You Believe? .......................... 62

06  Conceiving & Birthing The Supernatural ... 82

07  I Birth Fearless ..................................... 94

08  I Birth Pain-Free ................................. 116

09  Fearless Faith ...................................... 128

10  Renewing The Mind ............................ 140

11  Standing On His Promises ................... 154

12  God Is My Source ................................ 164

13  Restoring Hope & Faith After Disappointment ... 180

14  Aligning The Physical & Spiritual ........ 188

# Introduction

My name is Nissa Andrews, and I want to ask you a question. Would you believe me if I told you that you could birth your babies completely pain-free and naturally without using drugs? Would you think that is even possible?

Well, I'm here to tell you that you can. I have done it. I have birthed four babies, completely pain-free! I know you may be thinking; this woman is either lying or has a special superhuman gift. The truth is, I do have a special superhuman gift, and His name is Jesus! If you have Jesus, I am no different than you. We have the same supernatural abilities and anointing, for we have the same anointed one in us. If you do not know Jesus yet, I pray that my testimony will open your heart to seek Him and find the truth.

I wrote this book with a great sense of urgency in my heart and spirit. I have been sharing my birthing testimonies for 15 years and have had countless women ask me to teach them all that God showed me through my journey. I taught many classes out of my home. I've seen women grab hold of the truth that we are no longer under the curse of painful childbirth because Jesus redeemed us from the curse by becoming a curse for us. Many have experienced pain-free childbirth as well and have been sharing the good news with others. I was happy to leave it there. It was comfortable and safe.

Then the Lord spoke to me and said, "I have called you to raise up a generation of fearless women." Like Sarah, I laughed in my heart. Like Gideon, I'm looking around thinking, me, I'm the worst choice, God. There are so many powerful women in this world. Certainly, there is someone better suited for this job. Besides God, you know my reservations about ministry.

The points I was making didn't seem to matter to God one bit. He repeated Himself to me again, "Nissa, I have called you to raise up a generation of fearless women." This time something stirred in my spirit. The focus came off of myself, and my inabilities and my spirit lined up with what the Spirit of God was saying. My inabilities and reservations became obsolete in the presence of the God of Impossibilities.

I am writing this book because I heard God's voice, and I'm responding to Him with a willing and obedient heart. Beautiful women, you were not designed by God to live under the curse of fear, pain, and sickness. Let's start living a life of victory.

# Motherhood

### A poem by Christianna Maas

My willingness to carry life is the revenge, the antidote, the great rebuttal of every murder, every abortion, and every genocide. I sustain humanity. Deep inside of me, life grows. I am death's opposition.

I have pushed back the hand of darkness today. I have caused there to be a weakening tremor among the ranks of those set on earth's destruction. Today a vibration that calls angels to attention echoed throughout time. Our laughter threatened hell today.

I dined with the greats of God's army. I made their meals and tied their shoes. Today, I walked with greatness, and when they were tired, I carried them. I have poured myself out for the cause today.

It is finally quiet, but life stirs inside of me. Gaining strength, the pulse of life sends a constant reminder to both good and evil that I have yielded myself to Heaven and now carry its dream. No angel has ever had such a privilege, nor any man. I am humbled by the honor. I am great with destiny.

I birth the freedom fighters. In the great war, I am a leader of the underground resistance. I smile at the disguise of my troops, surrounded by a host of warriors, destiny swirling, invisible yet tangible, and the anointing to alter history. Our footsteps marking land for conquest, we move undetected through the common places.

Today I was the barrier between evil and innocence. I was the gatekeeper, watching over the hope of mankind, and no intruder trespassed. There is not an hour of day or night when I turn from my post. The fierceness of my love is unmatched on earth.

And because I smiled instead of frowned, the world will know the power of grace. Hope has feet, and it will run to the corners of the earth because I stood up against destruction.

I am a woman. I am a mother. I am the keeper and sustainer of life here on earth. Heaven stands in honor of my mission. No one else can carry my call. I am the daughter of Eve. Eve has been redeemed. I am the opposition of death. I am a woman.

# Humble Beginnings

# CHAPTER 1

For as long as I can remember, I wanted to be a mother. That was always the greatest desire of my heart. I dreamed of getting married and having a lot of children. A supernatural pain-free labor is not something I had desired or ever thought about because I had never heard of such a thing before.

Before I became pregnant with my first, I had a preconceived notion that labor pretty much sucks. The world says it's going to be awful and extremely painful. Writhing in pain and begging for drugs is what friends, family, movies, and social media told me. I heard it all and believed that was the way it's supposed to be.

The world has normalized pain, fear, and danger as a part of childbirth. As women, we have been trained and taught to partner with painful childbirth. They say, "just grin and bear it, but don't worry; you will forget all about it when you're holding your precious baby." I am in the same world like you and have grown up with all these same stories, so what changed my mind? How did I go from thinking a painful birth was the destiny of womanhood to knowing and experiencing four pain-free supernatural births?

This book's purpose is to take you through my journey of breaking free from the world system of what birthing looks like and exchanging it for the Kingdom, His righteousness, and what God intended for all women to experience. I can't wait to share all that the Lord brought me through and taught me along the way. We overcome the evil one through the blood of the Lamb and the word of our testimony.

My heart is for all women to experience how incredible labor, delivery, and pregnancy can be. My experience made me love every aspect of it. I loved it so much that I looked forward to being pregnant and doing it all over again each time. I received so much freedom during these years. It drew me closer to the Lord and opened my heart to deep revelation-knowledge of my life in Christ Jesus. I have no fear surrounding pregnancy and childbirth. It was such an incredible and empowering experience. I pray my story will not only inspire you but lead you into a deeper relationship with the Lord.

When you allow the Holy Spirit into your life's most intimate parts, you are destined for greatness and success. He is the most excellent teacher, always revealing incredible things. Things we didn't know we needed to know.

"Call to me, and I will answer you and show you great and mighty things, which you do not know." Jeremiah 33:3

# My Story

I'll start by sharing my journey with you. I was young, full of fear, insecurities, and self-hatred. I was also bitter, offended, and had unforgiveness in my heart. That was not an excellent start. My story should give you all hope. If God can do what He did in me, He certainly can do it for you too!

I rededicated my life to God in my late teens, and I wanted to live completely sold out for Jesus. I started reading my Bible and desired to hear from God. Later, I met and fell in love with my husband, Ryan, and we were married when I was 21.

I recognized that I had unhealthy, dysfunctional behaviors. Marriage has a way of bringing these things to the surface. Although I had received Jesus in my life, I needed the full revelation of what it meant to be a new creation and walk in it fearlessly. The most important keys to this were renewing my mind and radical obedience to God's voice. The driving force (at that time) that made me want to get healthy was my future generations. I wanted to be healthy emotionally, physically, and spiritually to pass down good traits to my future children.

Coming from a divorced and dysfunctional family, I didn't want to repeat what I experienced. I thought that if I could stop the dysfunction with me or at least make a significant difference, my children and my children's children would reap the benefits of what I uprooted and intentionally planted. How was I to teach my children how to live a victorious life if I wasn't walking in victory?

As soon as Ryan and I were married, I had pregnancy on my mind. I was excited to get pregnant, and after one year of marriage, I was ready. I began to prepare mentally by working on my insecurities and self-hatred. However, the more I tried, the worse it got. The problem was, I was trying to do it in my strength. I was working from the outside in. I needed to let the truth of God's word and His love take root in my heart, renew my mind, and then my actions would follow the rhythm of God's heart. Everything began to change when I made that shift. That is when I started to see a real transformation in my life. I spent countless hours with the Lord immersing myself in His presence. I got to know the voice of the Lord, and I began to hear him speak deep things to me. These are years I will cherish forever.

I thought as soon as I was ready to have kids that I would be pregnant right away. Months went by, and I was still not pregnant. I continued to press into God. I was so hungry for Him and His presence and longed to hear His thoughts. I hung on to every word He spoke to me. At the same time, I continued to cry out to God to become pregnant.

Then one day, in the middle of worship at church, I got caught up in a vision. I was on the floor in deep worship. I don't remember anyone else in the room, just me and God. In this vision, I saw a baby in my womb. God spoke very personally and in great depth to me regarding this. In a nutshell, He told me that I would be pregnant, that I would have a son, and that I was to name him Ezekiel. He spoke promises to my heart in regards to this. Promises over my family. Things that I didn't even fully understand then. Time stood still. It was such a holy moment. As soon as I got home, I wrote everything down. I wanted to be pregnant more than anything.

After the vision and the word I received from the Lord, I assumed I would get pregnant right away. Month after month of expectancy, and then disappointment seemed ongoing. Then one month, I finally got a positive pregnancy test! We were overjoyed. The promise had arrived. We were so excited we told all our family right away. Then three weeks later, I miscarried. I was so confused. How could this be? I know what God promised me. Why did this happen? I had so many questions. I was so disappointed. I kept crying out to God, "I want children; why am I not having children? Why did I miscarry? What's wrong with me? Did I even hear You correctly?" I know some of you have gone through heartbreak and discouragement of infertility and miscarriage. I want you to know that God is faithful. I am a living testimony of somebody who cried out to the Lord to have children, and He answered my prayers. I have four beautiful children now. He will do the same for you!

A couple of scriptures God gave me for miscarriage and barrenness that I stood on and declared until this truth became unshakable are:

### Exodus 23:25-26
*"Worship the Lord your God, and His blessing will be on your food and water. I will take away sickness from among you, and none will miscarry or be barren in your land. I will give you a full life span."*

### Deut. 7: 13-14
*"And He will love you and bless you and multiply you; He will also bless the fruit of your womb and the fruit of your land, your grain and your new wine and your oil, the increase of your cattle and the offspring of your flock, in the land of which He swore to your fathers to give you. You shall be blessed above all peoples; there shall not be a male or female barren among you or among your livestock."*

The Lord answered me one night as I continued to cry out to Him, and He said, "Not only are you going to be pregnant and have children, but you will give birth easily and pain-free. You will have great pregnancies, and you won't have any morning sickness."

I remember when I heard Him say this, it was quite a stretch for me. First of all, I had never heard of such a thing, and secondly, I just had a miscarriage. All I want is to be pregnant. This time God told me that I would have children and described how I would have them. It was a stretch for my mindset, but I did receive the word with great enthusiasm. I asked God to help me get my mind right about getting pregnant and having pain-free labor. It would take a total paradigm shift.

When God said that I was going to have children once again, my spirit leaped inside me, but at the same time, my circumstances were showing me something else. I wasn't getting pregnant. Then God led me to Jeremiah 1:4; *"Then the word of the Lord came to me, saying: 'Before I formed you in the womb I knew you; Before you were born I sanctified you; I ordained you a prophet to the nations.'"*

This verse came alive to me at that moment. I heard God saying to me, "Ezekiel has not been formed in your womb, yet I know him. He hasn't been born yet, but has already been set apart and sanctified. I want you to name his middle name Jeremiah." I felt an impression to look up the meaning of that name. Jeremiah's name may mean "Yahweh exalts" or "Yahweh loosens the womb," depending on the Hebrew root with which the name is associated. So my firstborn, whom I haven't met, but God knows, was to be named Ezekiel (God strengthens or God's strength) Jeremiah (Yahweh loosens the womb).

This name is prophetic, for this whole journey was a time of God teaching me strength. Not just any kind of strength, the God kind of strength. I knew God would loosen my womb. Every time I would think about getting pregnant again, I would prophesy the name, Ezekiel Jeremiah. I thanked God for him, even though I couldn't see him physically yet.

I find it fascinating that God named my son. Nothing God does is an accident. It is purposeful and carries power. In the Bible, when God changed a person's name and gave them a new name, it was usually to establish a new identity. God changed Abram's name to Abraham, which means father of a multitude. He changed his wife Sarai's name to Sarah, which means mother of nations. The name change happened one year before Isaac was born.

God gives life to the dead and calls those things which do not exist as though they did (*Romans 4:17*). Abram and Sarai needed to partner with what God was calling forth in them through their words and what they spoke. Now every time they said their new names, they were prophesying and declaring their future. They were pulling their supernatural prophetic word into the natural realm. Once they began to speak the truth of who they were despite their circumstances, something shifted. That same year Sarah became pregnant and birthed Isaac.

I continued to prophesy over myself by speaking my son's name, Ezekiel Jeremiah. Every time I said that name, I knew God was instilling strength in me. Strength to believe, strength to partner with Him, strength to push through every obstacle that stood in my way. I knew that it didn't matter what was going right or wrong with my womb. My womb would be loosed, by Yahweh, himself. Every time I spoke this name, the power of my true reality (God's Word) would shake off every lie, doubt, and disappointment, for the word of God is the highest authority.

I would be lying if I said I just believed, ran with it, and never had moments of feeling failure or weakness. The truth is that after God spoke these powerful words to me, I began to doubt my ability to hear Him. I had just had a miscarriage when God told me that I would have children and pain-free labors. The doubts didn't happen right away but started to show up in the waiting, especially after a miscarriage. I didn't doubt God or His ability as much as I began to doubt myself and my ability to hear Him correctly. I believe the enemy uses this tactic for many.

Instead of wallowing in my self-doubt, I decided to talk to God about it. I was honest with Him. I told Him I didn't doubt Him, but I wasn't so sure of myself. I remember thinking maybe I was making all this up because I wanted to be pregnant so bad. I did hear a still small voice about it all and even had a vision, but was it indeed the voice of God, or was it myself?

In my talk with God, I asked Him to do something for me. I asked, "God, if this truly was you speaking to me, can you somehow confirm it to me? I promise if you do this, I will never question if it's your voice ever again. I will confidently know what your voice sounds like forever. I feel somewhat ashamed to even ask this of you because of my weakness, but I know that you are good." I'm not saying this is the best thing to do, but it was real and raw and all I knew to do at that moment. I needed to assure my heart before Him.

Two weeks after this prayer, a woman comes up to me that I did not know at our church. We were a part of a large church with a few thousand people. My husband and I were the Jr. High Pastors at this time and were always in the youth building, which was separate from the main building. This particular Sunday, a woman comes to the Jr. High building holding a little present and asks to speak to me. I thought it was one of the parents.

As we moved somewhere more private, she begins to tell me that she believed she had a message from God for me. Now I'm leaning in. She continues to tell me that she is an intercessor and not someone who gives words, so she is nervous and is stepping out of her comfort zone.

She proceeded to tell me that every night for a week while she was interceding, my face popped up, so she would pray for me. She said it continued to happen night after night until she finally asked God, "what are you trying to tell me about this girl?" She then said, "God spoke to me to tell you something. God said that you are going to have a son, his name is Ezekiel, you have heard the voice of God, and everything He has spoken to you will come to pass."

I began to weep. The only person who knew what the Lord spoke to me was my husband. I never told anyone else what God had said or the name God gave me. Ryan was the only one I shared these intimate details with, and I knew this was God's voice through this woman. She sighed in relief, realizing that her stepping out in faith was deeply ministering to me. She then held up the present and handed it to me.

I opened up the gift to find a pair of newborn baby boy booties. She said, "These booties are important to me. They were my son's who is now a teenager, and I have been saving them to give to him one day. God told me that you were to have them so that any time doubt comes, you can look at these and know that God is faithful to His promise." I still have those precious booties today. I was floored, overjoyed, and so very grateful. We serve such a gracious, loving, merciful God. He is alive, and He speaks and wants to make Himself known to you.

A few weeks after I received that great confirmation, I happened to visit my brother's church. Many people he and I went to Bible college with also attended there. When I arrived, many of them came over to say hello and congratulate me on my pregnancy. My brother was so excited about becoming an uncle he shared the news with them, but they didn't get the memo that I had miscarried apparently.

It felt awkward as I needed to inform them that I was no longer pregnant. I think they also felt uncomfortable as they watched me fight back my tears. At that moment, one of the girls said, "Wait, right here. There is a book in our bookstore that I'm going to get for you." When she came back, she handed me the book Supernatural Childbirth by Jackie Mize. When I got home that afternoon, I started to read it. To my amazement, it confirmed the word God had spoken to me.

I was so excited I started reading it to my husband. I said, "Ryan, look, there is another woman who had received a word from the Lord that she would have easy labors too." God is so kind and so good. He gives us everything we need to be successful. My faith increased even more.

God was doing an excellent job of convincing me that I was encountering Him and hearing Him clearly. It was at this point that something shifted dramatically. I became an unshakable force to any mindset that opposed the word from the Lord. I was fully persuaded, and nothing anyone said was going to get me to change my mind.

# The Great Exchange

# CHAPTER 2

On the day of my future son Ezekiel's vision, there were many things spoken to me that I wanted to hear, and then some things I didn't want to hear. God told me I needed to forgive my dad. I had been estranged from my father since I was 15 years old. We hadn't seen or spoken to each other in nine years. When God said I needed to forgive my dad, I remember arguing with the Lord that I had already done so. I knew in my heart of hearts that wasn't really true. I was angry and bitter.

God asked me to forgive my dad and to restore my relationship with him. Ok, God, you are taking this too far, I thought. "I can forgive someone and not be in a relationship with them, right?" God replied, "Yes, you can, but I am asking you to restore your relationship with him." I wrestled with this for a few weeks. I thought I was living in forgiveness towards my dad. I was a Christian, I read my Bible, and I prayed for forgiveness, releasing my father on multiple occasions. That is why I felt bold arguing with God about the matter. I was adamant that I forgave him already. God was adamant that I needed to forgive him and restore my relationship with him.

I was very reluctant. I had a whole checklist of reasons I shared with God on why having a relationship with my dad wasn't a good idea. God remained silent. His silence to my list irritated me. I kept repeating the list as if He didn't hear me. Maybe I need to explain better. Silence remained. Now I'm getting frustrated. Hello, can you hear me? Why are you ignoring my pleas? This time as I read off my checklist, the revelation came. I haven't genuinely forgiven from my heart. My list of why I couldn't restore my relationship with my father became a mirror reflecting my heart's actual condition. How could I have been so blind? I had been deceiving myself for years.

During those weeks of wrestling over what God said, someone gave me the book Bait of Satan by John Bevere. They had no idea what God spoke to me. I devoured the whole book in 2 days. It strengthened me to walk in obedience towards restoring my relationship with my dad. I prayed to God and said, "Ok, I'll do what you are asking me to do, but I need help. First of all, I don't know how to get a hold of my dad. There is no way I'm going to get his information from any family members because that will stir up a hornet's nest, and I'm not ready for that yet. God, if this is something you want me to do, help me find my dad."

The same week I prayed that prayer, God answered. That Sunday, I went to church as usual. After the service ended, a lady approached me and said I heard who your father is and how she knew that I had no idea. I avoided telling anyone who my dad was. She proceeds to tell me that she worked at TBN and wrote down my dad's address and phone number for me if I ever wanted to get a hold of him. Then she handed me the info and said, "I felt from the Lord that you were to receive this." I just stared at her in shock, received it, said thank you, and walked away. When I got in my car, I wept.

To make a long story short, I called my dad. He was excited that I called him. It turned out he only lived 20 minutes from me, and I never knew it. The restoration process made me face all my fears and all my "reasons." The first night I saw my dad, something supernatural happened. The bondage of unforgiveness completely left. I felt free! My heart swelled with love and mercy towards my dad. My heart transformed, and my actions became so different. We saw each other for the first time in nine years, and I had changed so much. I was now married. We missed out on sharing some of these beautiful moments together. He didn't attend my wedding because I didn't invite him, and he didn't get to give me away.

He began to bring up the past and asked me to forgive him. I said," Dad, I have already forgiven you, the past is in the past, and this is a new day. Let's never discuss the past again. Let's enjoy our future. I love you." From that day forward, we had a fantastic relationship. I had the best time with my dad. We became very close. I'm moved to tears as I write this because my father passed away.

If I never said yes to God, I would have allowed the enemy to rip me off my whole life. I wouldn't have ever experienced the great relationship I had with my father in the last fifteen years. I would have remained bitter, angry, resentful, and untrusting. These are traits that were affecting everything in my life, especially my relationship with my husband. So much healing happened from saying yes to God. It unraveled me to the core. I exchanged shame, disappointment, fear, confusion, lies, bitterness, and unforgiveness for confidence, peace, power, joy, love, mercy, and a sound mind.

Before you assume that it all was just a fairy tale for me, let me clarify. These were some of the greatest and yet hardest years I have faced. I lost relationships with family members for seasons because they couldn't understand why I would have a relationship with my dad and didn't agree with me. I was misunderstood, rejected, and mistreated. I went through many trials. Trials that drove me deeper into the heart of God and produced patience and character. It wasn't easy on every front, but I saw God move powerfully in and through me.

Why do I share this vulnerable story? Unforgiveness was keeping me bound and affected my ability to get pregnant. I am not saying that every woman who has trouble getting pregnant is holding unforgiveness. However, in my case, it affected me. Unforgiveness is bondage. It keeps us captive and imprisoned. If there were any freedom in unforgiveness, we wouldn't need to be forgiven.

God knew what I needed to do to get the result for which I was praying. As I stated before, I wanted to get healthy for my future generations. Little did I know at the time, it would start the day I allowed my dad back into my life. I learned a powerful lesson through this as I look back. We often pray, asking God for specific things. In my case, I continually asked for children, a healthy family, to feel whole, and to have a great marriage. We say our part to God, but in some cases, when He speaks, we are unwilling to do what He says.

His promises are so good. Jesus tells us in Mark 11 that we can have whatever we say if we believe and don't doubt. Believe that you receive them. And whenever you are praying, if you have anything against anyone, forgive him.

### Mark 11:22-26

"So Jesus answered and said to them, "Have faith in God. For assuredly, I say to you; whoever says to this mountain, 'Be removed and be cast into the sea,' and does not doubt in his heart, but believes that those things he says will be done, he will have whatever he says. Therefore I say to you, whatever things you ask when you pray, believe that you receive them, and you will have them. "And whenever you stand praying, if you have anything against anyone, forgive him, that your Father in heaven may also forgive you your trespasses. But if you do not forgive, neither will your Father in heaven forgive your trespasses."

Forgiveness and prayer go hand in hand. Forgiveness is also mentioned in the Lord's prayer. Our salvation is not dependant on works and if we forgive others. We are looking at it wrong if we go about it with that mindset. Our ability to forgive others speaks to the evidence of our salvation. Freely we have received, freely give. The forgiveness we received at the cost of the blood of Jesus should be evident. It is evident through our actions in freely forgiving anyone who has wronged us.

If I disobeyed God's voice and continued my life with my heart in the same unforgiving state, unwilling to make the changes He was so kindly pointing out to me, I would have never received my desired result. He was not withholding anything from me; instead, I was withholding goodness from myself. God heard the cry of my heart and directed me where to start. It was up to me to say yes or no. It was my choice. I had no idea that's what was happening at the time. It didn't make sense to me then.

I now know why God asked me to do this. God is so wise, loving, and kind. Even if what He says doesn't make sense at the time, I implore you not to dismiss it. Even if it is hard and feels risky, do it! God knows what He is doing. Trust Him. He is trustworthy and faithful. He is leading you to possess the desires of your heart.

# Prayer of Forgiveness

Abba Father, thank you for your gift of forgiveness. Your mercy flows to me despite my faults, shortcomings, and failures. Freely I have received, so freely I give. I choose to forgive _____.

Thank you for Your grace, which empowers me to display unconditional love even to those who have hurt me. Even though I feel scarred and afraid, I choose not to let emotions control my actions. I release every hurt and choose to begin to love as Jesus loves.

I want to see _____ through Your eyes. Help me find the compassion that comes with true forgiveness. Thank you for complete freedom from the bondage of holding unforgiveness. I release it all to you.

In Jesus' name, amen.

# SELF-HATRED

Self-hatred also affected my ability to conceive. It is one of the most deadly forms of cursing yourself. The effects are incredibly damaging. I suffered from self-hatred, self-rejection, rejection of my body, and my womanhood for many years. It is an oppressive spirit.

Saying anything kind or good about myself was foreign. I did not know how to love myself. I repeatedly tore myself down. I would say things like, "you are stupid, you are ugly, something is wrong with you, I hate my periods and my womanhood; it's a curse. I hate my body—you're fat. You are no good," to name just a few. Not only did I speak these things over myself, but I believed them to be true.

I did not realize how damaging it was until we had a special speaker come to our church one Sunday. He made a statement about self-hatred that made me stop in my tracks. He said that he had seen incredible healings of autoimmune diseases when people rebuked the spirit of self-hatred, transformed their thinking about themselves, and renewed their minds. This statement was like one of David's stones being swung at me and hitting me right in the head to tear down this demonic stronghold and giant over my mind. When I heard it, I knew it was a warning. Tearing myself down for so many years would cause my body to tear itself down. Attacking myself would cause my body to attack itself. You reap what you sow.

I was horrified when I understood this because I was all about getting healthy. I had already dramatically changed my overall diet because I didn't feel that great physically. I had no idea that my words and thoughts could be a significant factor in my physical health. I wanted freedom in this area because it is bondage. An abundant life is my portion, and I wanted to walk in it fully over every area. I was getting serious about pulling down strongholds in my life. I asked God to help me get freedom from this and walk me through each step.

He is so faithful and is such a good Shepard. If you struggle with any of these things, ask God to help you walk into freedom and live victoriously over self-hatred. God sent His only begotten Son to die for you. He resurrected and put everything under His feet for our salvation, freedom, and inheritance. God wants you to get the revelation of our freedom in Christ, and He will speak to you, reveal things to you, and guide you. He wants you to prosper and be in good health just as your soul prospers. He is the God of breakthrough, victory, and freedom.

**I asked God to teach me:**

- ✝ Teach me how you see me.

- ✝ Teach me how to bless my body.

- ✝ Teach me how to renew my mind on my worth and my value.

- ✝ Teach me how to love myself.

- ✝ Teach me the power of my words and how to set a guard over my mouth.

- ✝ Teach me how to speak life over myself.

- ✝ Teach me how to walk in truth and how to tear down every lie.

I believe self-hatred and cursing my body was the root of my miscarriage. My body was responding to my continual self-rejection. I radically went after a breakthrough in this area. It started with repenting over my actions towards myself and to God. From that day forward, I turned from my wicked ways toward myself.

Wicked is a powerful word, but how I treated myself was downright nasty. If anyone treated or spoke to my daughter the same way I was treating myself, I would think it was malicious behavior, so let us call it what it is.

I saw a dramatic change in myself and my actions when I made the shift. I was happier, more content, and felt so great. My health took a turn for the best. All the ailments that bothered me completely went away. I had my cellular levels tested, and they went from very low to very high pretty quickly after this revelation.

Not only that, I saw a dramatic change in my periods (menstrual cycle). I use to have debilitating periods. The cramps were unbearable, and I bled so heavily for seven days. I couldn't survive without Midol and a heating pad. I missed countless days at school and work over these symptoms. I dreaded my period every month and would curse my body, saying things like I hate being a girl.

When I stopped cursing my body, to my surprise and delight, my periods started getting better. I felt less and less pain every time, and the bleeding wasn't as heavy as it used to be. Now I can hardly even notice when I'm about to start. My body was responding to the truth and my newfound freedom. The difference after one year was quite shocking.

Self-hatred is a demonic stronghold that should not be allowed to take residence in your mind, will, and emotions. You have the authority to evict that stronghold. Do you not know that your bodies are members of Christ? How dare I tear down Christ.

Oh, the audacity of this foul antichrist spirit. This spirit opposes the very members of Christ, us His body. *"My body is the temple of the Holy Spirit who is in me, and I am not my own, for I was bought with a price. Therefore, glorify God in your body and in your spirit, which are God's" (1 Corinthians 6: 19-20).*

When I saw self-hatred for what it was, it became easy for me to uproot that out of my life and cast it into the sea. I was no longer willing to partner with an antichrist spirit any longer.

# Prayer For Releasing Self-Hatred

Abba Father,

Thank you for being near to me. You are near to the brokenhearted and save the crushed in spirit. I give my crushed spirit to you and exchange it for the Spirit of power, of love, and a sound mind. I break agreement with every lie I have come to believe about myself.

I repent for giving satan permission to torment me in my mind and through my own words. From this day forward, I will love myself as You love me and speak blessings over myself and not curses. I turn from using my tongue to obey satan to speak words of death and choose to follow the Holy Spirit to utter words of life over myself.

I take up the authority given to me by Jesus and command all dark powers assigned to steal, kill, and destroy me to leave now in Jesus' name. You can no longer bring me down into self-hatred. Your day is over. Today I choose to live through Jesus Christ and declare that I will walk in pure Agape love towards myself and others.

In Jesus' name, Amen!

# Loving Your Pregnant Body

Loving your body isn't about looking perfect or measuring up to worldly standards, but about treating your body well by speaking life-giving words over yourself. Ditch critical and comparative thoughts. Instead, embrace that God created you with wisdom. Your body is good and divinely designed. God doesn't make mistakes.

I dare you to start looking daily at your body naked in a mirror while blessing every part. During pregnancy, your body is a vessel for life. Revel in the aliveness of your body and its ability to accommodate your pregnancy. Celebrate your growing belly, hips, breasts, and thighs. The Creator Himself made your beautiful body. Look in the mirror and announce the name of your designer: "Body by God!"

You have been given a mighty mission to house, feed, nurture, and protect your growing baby. What a miracle! What a joy!

# Rejoice In The Truth

I am fearfully and wonderfully made.
*Psalm 139:14*

I am made in God's image and likeness.
*Genesis 1:26*

I am God's masterpiece.
*Ephesians 2:10*

Everything God has made is very good (perfect),
including me.
*Genesis 1:31*

I am precious.
*Proverbs 31:10 & 1 Peter 2:4*

There is no flaw in me.
*Song of Solomon 4:7*

I am valuable.
*Luke 12:7*

My body is the temple of God.
*1 Corinthians 3:16*

| Lies Of The Enemy | | Truth From God |
|---|---|---|
| Unaccepted | ——◦——▷ | Accepted |
| Unwelcome | ——◦——▷ | Welcome |
| Unwanted | ——◦——▷ | Chosen |
| Unknown | ——◦——▷ | Included |
| Unworthy | ——◦——▷ | Worthy |
| Not good enough | ——◦——▷ | Approved |
| Worthless | ——◦——▷ | Precious |
| Rejected | ——◦——▷ | Called |

Release all lies you have believed about yourself and come into agreement with what God says about you. May God empower and strengthen you as you continue the journey of discovering who you are in Him.

# Supernatural Pregnancy

# CHAPTER 3

After three years of trying to get pregnant, the day finally came when I looked down and saw a positive pregnancy test. Ryan and I were so excited! My excitement turned into momentary fear as the experience of my miscarriage came flooding back to my mind. Lies were attached to these fears. Lies that said, don't get too excited because you might get disappointed again. Don't tell anyone because you don't want to go through the pain of telling everyone you aren't pregnant again. Be careful and do everything right, or you might lose this baby too, and so on. These thoughts brought torment and were ripping me off of experiencing joy and peace.

After a few weeks of listening to these lies, I noticed the fruit they were producing in my life: such as fear, no peace, and a lack of joy. I realized that those are not the fruit of the Spirit. The fruit of the Spirit is love, joy, peace, patience, kindness, goodness, faithfulness, and self-control. It was time to use some self-control and get a grip on my emotions.

Proverbs 25:28 says, "A person without self-control is like a city with broken-down walls."

Using self-control isn't meant only as a restraint for controlling yourself for others' sake. It is also there to protect you from foreign intruders. These foreign intruders include lies and any thoughts that oppose the kingdom of God and His Word. Don't let the word self-control confuse you into thinking this is a self-effort. We can't accomplish it on our terms. If we try to do it out of ourselves, it will always be a struggle, and we won't walk in victory. It takes a partnership with the Holy Spirit, for our warfare weapons are not carnal but are mighty in God.

I began to war in the Spirit to get a grip on my emotions. I did this by making sure I was armored up. How did I armor myself? The Bible told me how I should do it, and this is what it says.

*"Be strong in the Lord [draw your strength from Him and be empowered through your union with Him] and in the power of His [boundless] might. Put on the full armor of God [for His precepts are like the splendid armor of a heavily-armed soldier], so that you may be able to [successfully] stand up against all the schemes and the strategies and the deceits of the devil. For our struggle is not against flesh and blood, but against the rulers, against the powers, against the world forces of this [present] darkness, against the spiritual forces of wickedness in the heavenly (supernatural) places. Therefore, put on the complete armor of God, so that you will be able to [successfully] resist and stand your ground in the evil day, and having done everything [that the crisis demands], to stand firm [in your place, fully prepared, immovable, victorious]. So stand firm and hold your ground, having tightened the wide band of truth around your waist and having put on the breastplate of righteousness, and having strapped on your feet the gospel of peace in preparation [to face the enemy with firm-footed stability and the readiness produced by the good news]. Above all, lift up the [protective] shield of faith with*

*which you can extinguish all the flaming arrows of the evil one. And take the helmet of salvation, and the sword of the Spirit, which is the Word of God. With all prayer and petition at all times [on every occasion and in every season] in the Spirit, and with this in view, stay alert with all perseverance and petition [interceding in prayer] for all God's people ( Ephesians 6:10-17 AMP )."*

If our struggle is not against flesh and blood but spiritual forces of wickedness in heavenly places, we must war in the Spirit. What does spiritual warfare look like for a believer? Take note of the posture of the heavily armed soldier in this passage. He is resisting and standing, not fighting. The battle has already been won. Like him, we need to stand in victory. Putting on the "Armor of God" makes you successful at standing up to the enemy's schemes. Each armor piece holds truth, and each truth is a key of the Kingdom that Jesus gave us. It's time to put these truths into action by putting them on like armor. These truths are your protection against the enemy.

# Armor Up

First, gird yourself with the truth. It starts with righteousness. Not a sin consciousness, but a righteousness consciousness. That means you know who you are in Christ, Jesus, as well as your inheritance. Guard your heart against anything stealing this vital truth from you by putting on the breastplate of righteousness. If you don't have the full revelation of your righteousness in Christ, you will have difficulty resisting the devil and standing firm against his schemes.

The next thing you need to do is strap to your feet the gospel of peace, which makes us firm-footed and completely stable when facing the enemy. When we know that we are righteous, we are at peace, unmovable, firm footed. *"For the kingdom of God is righteousness, peace, and joy in the Holy Spirit." (Romans 14:17).* Those are your portion. When I recognized I was losing my peace and joy through the fear that was creeping in, I knew it was time to tighten the straps. If I was losing my peace, I realized I needed to renew my mind with the truth. Who am I in Christ?

The love Jesus poured out for us reminds me of who I am and casts out all fear. Fear's purpose is to loosen the straps of peace, making it easier to stumble. It makes us unstable. Don't yield to fear. Remember who you are and who is with you! Jesus said, *"Peace I leave with you, My peace I give to you; not as the world gives do I give to you. Let not your hearts be troubled, neither let it be afraid." (John 14:27)* You can stand firm and be full of peace because Jesus has given you, His peace. Take your inheritance of peace and strap it on. Don't allow it to get loose by letting your heart be troubled and afraid. Be confident that everywhere you walk; you have peace no matter the situation. And not just any peace, the peace of Jesus himself, the Prince of Peace.

Above all, lift up the shield of faith. The only way we receive all that Jesus has won for us is through faith. Believe and receive all these kingdom truths. Faith is also like drawing a line in the sand, leaving the natural realm, and stepping into the supernatural. God and His Word are above the enemy, and you have all of heaven backing you up. Nothing can consume God. Instead, our God is a consuming fire *(Hebrews 12:29)*. Put your faith in God, and every fiery dart that the enemy shoots your way will be quenched and consumed. Faith knows rewards are coming your way! *(Hebrews 11:6)*

In addition to faith, embrace the power of salvation's complete deliverance, like a helmet to protect your thoughts from lies. The weapon we use to accomplish this is the sword of the Spirit. The word of God helps us divide truth from lies. *"For the Word of God is living and powerful, and sharper than any two-edged sword, piercing even to the division of soul and Spirit, and of joints and marrow, and is a discerner of the thoughts and intents of the heart." (Hebrews 4:12).* The Word of God brings discernment and helps you divide the flesh from the Spirit so you can walk in the Spirit. *"For as many as are led by the Spirit of God; these are the sons of God." (Romans 8:14).* When it comes to the sword, wield and yield.

Last but certainly not least, pray always with all prayer in the Spirit. Praying in tongues is something we should be doing all the time. I saw a dramatic increase in my mood, perspective, revelation, and intimacy with God when I practiced speaking in tongues more. Communing with God, spirit to Spirit is a powerful thing. It bypasses our natural mind and brings us straight into the Spirit.

# Faith And Expectation

Once I made sure my armor wasn't falling off or missing, I took a step of faith and let everyone know I was pregnant. I told fear to take a hike and fully embraced the joy and expectation of this pregnancy. I also told everyone that this baby would be a boy. Many asked me, "but what if it's a girl?" I always replied, "This baby is not a girl; it is a boy. God told me so and already prepared me for him." They were concerned about my continual confession of having a boy when I didn't have the proof yet. They would say things like; you shouldn't keep saying that because she will feel unwanted if you are having a girl. Nobody understood why I was so convinced.

I did not doubt that I would birth Ezekiel Jeremiah. I displayed the baby booties on my bedroom dresser for a constant reminder of the faithfulness of God. He had spoken, I believed, and it came to pass.

Not one time in any of my pregnancies did I have morning sickness, just as God had spoken to me. That alone was huge since morning sickness was a big deal in my family. My sister had horrible morning sickness up to her seventh month of pregnancy with each of her kids. I thought terrible morning sickness was the fate of all the women in our family. God rewrote my story, and what a glorious story it is. I enjoyed every kind of food throughout my pregnancies and wasn't bothered by anything.

I felt fantastic, no matter how much weight I gained. I remained comfortable even up to the day of delivery. I gained about 35 pounds during each of the four pregnancies. Many told me not to eat spicy foods because it would cause heartburn and indigestion.

I love spicy foods and ate them anyway, without a problem. I never had sciatica, indigestion, or heartburn. I never had high blood pressure, and didn't have to deal with gestational diabetes or any pregnancy-related complications. I had no swelling. In fact, during all four of my pregnancies, I never even needed to remove my wedding ring. Sleep was also never an issue. I had no problem getting comfortable in bed during the night.

Even after birthing four children, I don't have one stretch mark. There is nothing wrong with stretch marks, but I find it supernatural that I have none. It didn't even cross my mind to pray not to get any. God just did it.

I loved pregnancy so much I could hardly wait to be pregnant again. Once, when I was eight months pregnant, I said to Ryan, "I can't wait to be pregnant again!", he looked at me and laughed so hard. He said, "Sweetheart, you are pregnant." I replied, "I know, but I'm at the end, and I'm going to miss being pregnant." He kept laughing, saying, "What woman says that? Only you, Nissa, only you!"

I hope that this story inspires you to think differently about pregnancy. Expect things to look different than what the world tells you. Pregnancy and birth are to be a blessing! God designed it that way. You are not meant to be sick, full of fear, and have complications. That is not God's will for you.

Pregnancy is supposed to be a blessed experience. You don't need to partner with sickness and all the pregnancy symptoms. You are a new creation. You are joint seated with Christ. We are part of a different kingdom and are not to be conformed to this world. We are different and should look different.

Instead of asking the world, social media, and google how you should feel and what to expect in pregnancy, take some time and ask God how He thinks you should feel during your pregnancy. What are His thoughts surrounding pregnancy? Write them down. His thoughts and words of life make wonderful declarations.

# TWO TRIALS

I experienced two trials in pregnancy. The first was with my firstborn son, Ezekiel. Towards the end of my pregnancy, my midwife became concerned and wanted me to get ultrasounds to check on him. She thought I had IGR (Intrauterine growth retardation) and told me Ezekiel had stopped growing. Each week I would get an ultrasound, only to have the midwife scratch her head and send me off to get another. Fear tried to grip my heart and take hold of my thoughts once again.

I strengthened myself in the Lord and remembered my armor.

We had finished three ultrasounds, and the midwife was writing us up a new one. Ryan and I stood in her office and declared boldly this time, "there will be no more ultrasounds." She looked up from writing the note with shock and said, "excuse me." We declared again with boldness and certainty, "there will not be another ultrasound. Our son is fine. He is healthy and is growing. He will be a perfect weight." This statement wasn't just a declaration to us; this is what we believed.

I knew the enemy was coming after the word of God over my life, and I wasn't about to let him have it. My midwife put her pen down and said we could forgo the next ultrasound for now. She never spoke another word to us again after that day about the IGR, and we never mentioned it either. I'm not sure what caused the shift in her, but I know after I birthed Ezekiel, the first thing she said to us was that he was much bigger than she expected.

The second trial I faced during pregnancy was with my daughter. At about ten weeks, I woke up one morning bleeding heavily. It was not looking good in the natural. I grew in understanding my authority in Christ by this time and rose in the midst of it.

My neighbors may have heard me telling the devil off that day. I was pulling no punches. Like a lion, I declared, 'Fear I will not partner with you on any level, for the Spirit of God is in me. I am a mighty woman of God, and I know how to wield my sword.' I grabbed my Bible and told the devil; it is written that 'no one shall suffer miscarriage or be barren in the land.' (Exodus 23:26). I will not suffer a miscarriage. It is written, 'He has blessed your children within you.' (Psalm 147:13). This baby is blessed within me. The fruit of my womb is blessed (Deuteronomy 28:4).

God, you have formed this baby's inward parts and knitted her together in this womb. Your eyes have seen her unformed substance, and in Your book is written all the days that are appointed for this child (Psalm 139: 13-16). Devil, you can not steal, kill, and destroy from my womb. This baby will live and fulfill every appointed day You have predestined. This baby will not die but live and declare the works of the Lord (Psalm 118:17). Bleeding stop right now in the name of Jesus. Body, you are blessed, fruitful, and will not suffer a miscarriage in Jesus' name. I rejoice in the truth and my inheritance!"

After I told the devil off and made him out to be a liar, I put on some praise and worship and danced with joy even though the bleeding continued. I worshipped and prayed in the Spirit despite how it looked in the natural. That night my bleeding completely stopped and never returned. I had a full-term pregnancy and birthed my beautiful daughter, Glory.

# My Pain-Free Birth Testimonies

# CHAPTER 4

I am excited to share my four pain-free birth testimonies. I pray these stories will build your faith in what is possible for childbirth. Our testimony in Christ Jesus is a powerful thing. Revelation 12:11 says, "they (us) triumphed over him (the Devil) by the blood of the Lamb and the word of their testimony." Speaking about what Jesus has done for us glorifies God and destroys the enemy's works.

## EZEKIEL'S BIRTH

This testimony is great because even when things went wrong according to what we had planned, it shows how everything can still go so right. With Ezekiel's labor, everything went wrong in the sense that I had planned on delivering him at a birthing center but didn't end up there in the end. Even though I had a midwife, I was not comfortable with having my baby at home. We lived in an apartment, and I thought it might bother the neighbors if there was a lot of commotion in the middle of the night. We decided on the birthing center instead. I made plans and had many thoughts on how it was going to go down.

Surprisingly, my water broke first, which was unexpected. I always assumed my water would break at the end of labor. The midwife swept my membranes a week before the due date, and I believe it weakened my sac. I decided after that experience; never to allow a membrane sweep again.

Even though my water broke first and labor didn't start the way I imagined, all of the preparation throughout the nine months of being pregnant kept me calm and in total peace. I was confident that everything was going to be perfect and that the labor would be pain-free.

It all started at 5 a.m when my husband and I were still sleeping in bed. I remember waking up thinking that I had peed myself but realized quickly that my water had broken. Today was the day!! I felt great, got up, and decided to get ready. Mother's Day happened to be the following day, and I still needed to buy a gift for my mom. I put on a pad to catch water leakage, and off, Ryan and I went shopping to buy gifts for our mothers.

I was having sporadic contractions throughout the day but felt nothing but my stomach hardening like a rock. Ryan and I had a lot of fun that day. We bought the gifts that we needed, went for walks, and even went out to dinner.

The conversation with the waitress was hilarious. She asked when I was due, and I said I was actually in labor now and that my water already broke. We became the talk of the restaurant. In the meantime, my midwife was checking in with me on the phone. As day turned to night, she decided to come over and check on me since my water had broken early that morning.

When she arrived at 7 p.m, she wanted to see how dilated I was. She looked at me with concern on her face and said, "You're barely even dilated to a one. We need to get you progressing and in active labor, or you're going to deliver this baby in the hospital." When she spoke these words to me, some disappointment set in; how could I not be dilating? These are the kinds of things you don't want to hear when you're in labor. I knew the enemy was trying to sideline me by trying to get me to partner with a different outcome than what God had spoken.

It was time to put my renewed mind and faith into action and rise in my authority. The thoughts came that all my plans were going awry. I didn't want to have a hospital birth. I wanted to have the baby where I've planned; in the birthing center. Many thoughts came to mind.

The midwife suggested that I should take some castor oil. She said, "as you can see, you will be laboring a long time. Try to get some sleep, and I'll plan on coming back here at 6 a.m to check on you again. If you are not in active labor by then, we may need to send you to the hospital." She left at 8:30 p.m.

After the midwife left, Ryan went to the store to buy some castor oil, per the midwife's advice. When he got home, he said he would make me a castor oil smoothie. I looked at him, grabbed that bottle of oil, and said, "there is no need." I opened the lid and drank a bunch straight from the bottle. Ryan had a look of shock on his face.

I grabbed his hands, and we prayed together. I said out loud, "Nissa, you will not end up in the hospital." I commanded my body to start dilating right away and for labor to progress quickly and with ease. You will have this baby before 6 a.m, I proclaimed. I will not partner with a long, hard labor. After we prayed and declared what would take place, we decided to get some sleep.

About an hour after we went to bed, I woke up and knew something shifted. Things were progressing. The contractions felt more substantial and consistent. I started feeling nauseous from drinking all that castor oil and ended up vomiting all the dinner I ate. That wasn't pleasant, but I felt much better after that.

I walked around the apartment, commanding my body to continue dilating quickly. I felt great. The contractions became very strong, but there was no pain. I knew things were moving right along at this point. I asked Ryan to call my mom and tell her she could head over to the house now. Ryan took that request as a cue to also call the midwife. He asked me if we should go to the birthing center? "Do you think you are getting closer?" I told him I thought so but wasn't sure how far along I was. We figured it was a good time to call the midwife and let her know I was in active labor.

We called the midwife, and she agreed to meet us at the birthing center. Ryan started packing up the car. We weren't in a huge rush because we thought we had plenty of time. We waited to give my mom and the midwife enough time to arrive at the birthing center a little before we got there. We lived much closer, and they were 30 minutes away. A lot happened in those 30 minutes.

When we were about to leave, I had an urge to use the bathroom because I felt like I needed to poop. As I sat on the toilet, I realized I didn't actually have to go to the bathroom. I'm feeling the head. I yelled out to Ryan, "the baby is coming, the baby is coming!" I didn't even realize how far along I was the whole time. I had no idea that I was ready to deliver this baby.

We were now alone in the apartment together, and Ryan had a surprised look on his face as he tried to figure out what to do. He called the midwife, who was now almost at the birthing center. She rushed to our apartment instead. He put her on speakerphone as she directed my husband on what to do. I could hear the whole conversation. She said that I should lay down on my back on the bed since that might slow things down. Try to hold on for 10 minutes, and I will be there. She was asking if Ryan could see the head, and he could. I remember thinking, hold on, Nissa; she is almost here, don't push yet. Now looking back, I should have just delivered the baby.

When the midwife finally arrived, she came running in the door and threw on some gloves. She said, "ok, now you can push." When I pushed, she looked up at me and said, "you are pretty tight. I'm going to cut your perineum to help you ease the baby out." I said very boldly, "no, you will not. I'm going to squat, and this baby will come right out." She said we could try that first.

I got up from lying down on the bed and got in a squatting position. I had read that this position opens you up an extra inch. The Holy Spirit brought that to my remembrance and directed me in what to do. If I was tight, I knew this position would help.

As soon as I got into the squatting position, I birthed Ezekiel in 2 easy pushes. It was all completely pain-free. Ezekiel was born at 2 in the morning on Mother's day. It felt like an additional kiss from God. A great reminder that God gave me the desire of my heart to become a mother. He gave me the gift of motherhood, wrapped it in a big bow, and I held the physical promise of it all on Mother's Day!

After I birthed Ezekiel, the midwife checked me to see if I needed any stitches. To her surprise, I didn't even have one tear. Stitches were not necessary. Isn't that amazing? Supposedly I was so tight that the baby was having trouble coming out, according to the midwife. If I had agreed with letting her cut my perineum, I would have had a very different outcome. I am so happy I remained calm and in my authority during this labor. There were many opportunities for me to partner with fear, a voice other than God, and a different outcome.

I purposed in my heart not to be led by man or my natural man's thoughts, but by the Holy Spirit. With each significant moment, I could hear His still small voice telling me what to do. I silenced every voice but His. The result was that it worked every time. I experienced everything God told me I would. It didn't play out how I imagined it would, but the final result remained true to God's word over my life. My first birth experience was incredible. I enjoyed being at home and in my bed after all was said and done. I knew from here on out that I would be a home birth mom.

# GLORY'S BIRTH

For my second labor, we planned a home birth. Since I didn't realize how far along I was the last time, we figured it would be better to set up and prepare for delivery at home. We were in the process of moving, so I had found another midwife. This time I made sure she was a more natural, non-medical midwife.

We bought a house and were in escrow the last month of this pregnancy. We stayed with my In-laws, which was ten minutes from our new home, while we waited to move in. I was praying that we would be in our new place before I gave birth. My due date was quickly approaching. The house we bought was a foreclosure, so it needed a lot of work before we could move in. We were just five days out from moving into our new home when Glory decided to come. She came early.

Here I was in another situation that I didn't want. Laboring at my Father in-law's house was not ideal and a bit uncomfortable. What I came to realize is that it doesn't matter whether you have the perfect scenario or not. What matters is your internal reality. Your inner reality will always become your external reality.

I spent countless hours building my faith and renewing my mind on birthing. I felt strong and was ready. I had a peace that surpassed all understanding. I knew this to be true because my understanding was that I should be uncomfortable birthing at my father-in-law's house. However, all that went out the window. I had so much peace.

When Ryan and I got up the morning of Glory's birth, I told him I was pretty sure today was the day. I felt a change in my body but did not know if I was in labor yet. Ryan and his dad were planning to go to our new house to finish painting that day. Ryan asked if he should stay. I told him it was fine to go since I wasn't sure, but to listen for his phone if anything changes.

We had breakfast together, and at 8 in the morning, off they went. I called my midwife and put her on alert since she knew that Ryan and I almost birthed our first baby alone. I told her I had fast and easy labors. I also called my sister, who lived nearby, and told her I thought I was in labor. I asked her to come over to walk, get things moving, and see how I felt as the day progressed. She wanted to take a shower first and then would head over.

Thankfully my mother-in-law was home with me. I told her I thought today was the day and that my sister was coming over soon so we could go for a walk. She wanted to join us. I felt like taking a shower and wanted to get ready first. The midwife texted me before I got in the shower to let me know that she would be at the gym down the street from the house, so if anything changed quickly, she would be there in a heartbeat.

After being up in the bedroom for a little while, my mother-in-law came to check on me. I told her I didn't feel like walking anymore, which was probably the first clue that I was further along than I realized. She asked me if I had timed any of my contractions yet. I had not. We decided to time them.

Every time I felt a contraction, I let her know to start timing. We continued conversing with one another. As soon as I felt a contraction, I would say, "it's starting right now." Then I would tell her when it ended. I could talk through every contraction. After timing four contractions, she looked at me and said, "You need to call your midwife. Your contractions are very close together. They are a little over a minute long and 30 seconds apart."

Everything happened very fast from there. I called the midwife to tell her how fast things progressed, and Sharon called Ryan to ask him to come back. Ryan said that as soon as Sharon called him to come back, he knew he would miss Glory's birth if he didn't get to the house as quickly as possible.

Sharon stayed with me, and I decided I wanted to sit on the toilet. For some reason, I love laboring on the toilet at the end. Then I heard a commotion of Ryan and the midwife running upstairs together. They both arrived at the same time.

As they came in, I was walking over to the bed. Just then, my water broke, and I instantly felt the head. My midwife set her equipment down, and everyone started scrambling. I was birthing Glory while the midwife was trying to put her gloves on. She told Sharon to write down that my water broke, and the head was crowning at 11:14 a.m.

The midwife started catching the baby with one glove on while also asking Sharon to put the glove on her other hand. Meanwhile, Ryan is in the bathroom trying to scrub the paint off his hands, and Sharon is still trying to finish writing down the time for the midwife. We laugh about all this now. Everything happened so fast and was pretty comical.

Sharon ended up being a little bummed because she missed seeing Glory come out. While she was writing down 11:14, she heard me say, "Oh, there's my baby!" She turned around, and Glory was in my arms. I didn't even feel like I needed to push Glory out. It seemed like she just flew out. At 11:16 in the morning, Glory was born.

My labor from start to finish was maybe 2 hours. Again, I had no idea how far along I was. Honestly, it is hard to gauge when there is no pain. Even though Glory came out as fast as lightning, I didn't tear and needed not one stitch. I had just experienced my second fast, easy, supernatural, and pain-free birth.

As the midwife did all the paperwork at the kitchen table, she talked with Sharon and said what she witnessed was one in a million. My sister was amazed when she got the phone call that the baby had already been born. "How can this be? I just talked to Nissa one hour ago!" she said.

# LUKE'S BIRTH

At this point, I was extremely comfortable with pregnancy and labor. I felt like superwoman and was confident enough to birth the baby by myself without any help. I was so relaxed about everything that we decided to make this wild, crazy move to Hawaii at eight months pregnant. It is where God was leading us in this season.

We sold everything we owned and showed up on the island of Oahu with two kids, two pieces of luggage, no house, no jobs yet, and no midwife for my eight-month pregnant self. God said, go, and we went. Everything God did in this season was one miracle after another. A story to be told for another time.

We moved into a house a week after we arrived and bought a car. I ended up finding a midwife who decided that she would take me on even though I was almost at the end of my pregnancy. Ryan and I liked the thought of someone else taking care of all the cleanup and aftermath of birth, including the paperwork and documents.

My new midwife, Miriam, was a 70-year-old Jewish woman that was retiring from midwifery. I talked her into seeing me. I told her that I have very fast, easy labors and that with my first two births, my midwives showed up as I was birthing my babies. I promised her it would be easy for her. She decided I would be her last client.

Luke ended up arriving one week early. I started feeling a shift in my body the day I birthed him. I learned how to read my body better through experience. By the time I know for sure I'm in active labor, I have the baby soon after. We all agreed that I would let everyone know as soon as I thought I might be in labor. The midwife wanted to come in plenty of time to set up and not feel rushed for the birth. When the midwife arrived, I was cleaning my house and doing laundry. My mother-in-law was also there to help me settle into our new place before Luke arrived and help with the kids during my labor and recovery time.

An hour after Miriam arrived, I was making popcorn to have as a snack. She looked at me and said, "I'm all set up, and you seem like yourself. Are you sure you are in labor?" I told her I knew I was definitely in labor because this all felt familiar. She asked if she should go home and come back in a few hours. I replied, "If you go home now, you might not be here when I birth this baby. I will have this baby in a few hours." Her face said it all. She looked like she thought I was crazy. Nonetheless, she stayed.

A couple of hours later, I felt like talking and hanging out with everyone kept me from progressing faster. I snuck back into my bedroom and took a hot shower. That felt so good and was quite relaxing. When I got out of the shower, I enjoyed leaning over the sink countertop, holding up my body's weight with my arms through every painless contraction. I bent my knees and surrendered to each contraction fully.

All of a sudden, I felt Luke descending through the birth canal. I never experienced that sensation before. With all my other deliveries, I just felt the head suddenly. This time, I could feel him descending. It was really cool.

Instead of yelling out for everyone to come to me, I walked over to them in the other room and said very calmly and matter of fact, "The baby is coming now. Come into the bedroom." My husband makes fun of me for that now, and we laugh about it. I said those words, then turned around and went back into the bedroom. He said that the midwife looked at him like, is she serious? Ryan said when he looked at her, "we better hurry."

We had everything set up on the floor in my room because I figured I would birth Luke in the squatting position as I did with my other two. As I got into that position, it felt like everything just stopped including the contractions. I never experienced that before.

We waited for a few minutes and still nothing. The Holy Spirit told me to get back into the position I had of leaning over the sink, so I got up and walked over there. As soon as I leaned over the sink and bent my knees, I could feel Luke descending again, and then his head started crowning. After the first contraction that was pushing Luke out, my water broke. Change of plans, we are birthing him in the bathroom now. With the second push, Luke came out without one tear. From the moment I thought I might be in labor until I held Luke in my arms was seven hours. I experienced my third painless birth.

Two days after I delivered Luke, Miriam came to check on us. She looked at me and said, "I have to ask you a question. Did you experience any pain at all in your labor? Because from my view and from what I saw, it didn't look like you experienced any pain. You didn't even make any noises whatsoever. The most I heard was you exhaling softly as you were birthing Luke. I've been a midwife for forty years, and I've never seen anything like it."

At that moment, I was able to share Jesus with this sweet elderly Jewish woman. It was more than I think she could comprehend at the time. She wasn't so sure about Jesus, but she did express one thing, how I birthed was a miracle.

She ended up calling me a year later, out of the blue, to tell me that she would never forget me. She said that my birth was the highlight of her whole career, and even though she is now retired, if I had any more babies, she would deliver my baby for free. She wanted to be a part of another pain-free supernatural birth. She expressed that she wished every woman could experience birth the way that I do. I felt so humbled and honored to have left such a great impression on Miriam. Her words meant a lot to me. I saw that God was using my births to preach the good news of the gospel and inspire women no matter the age.

## MICAH'S BIRTH

My last and final birth was with my son Micah. We had recently moved to Redding, California, and were no longer living in Hawaii. Miriam's health was declining and her flying out to California was out of the picture, so we started our search for a new midwife. I found a spirit-filled midwife named Corrina that I loved! I shared, once again, that I have fast, easy labors.

Micah came two weeks early. This time I knew I was in labor because I had a bloody show. I love how every labor is different. When I had the bloody show, I told Ryan to gear up because today was the day. He ran a quick errand to get some baby diapers because we didn't even have those yet. Those due dates appear faster and faster with each additional child, especially when they come earlier than expected.

I called Corrina to let her know, and she came to the house. My older two children were still at school, and Luke was hanging out with me. Luke and I walked laps around the backyard together. After Luke's birth, I concluded that I mostly like to labor alone. When I'm alone, I feel like everything goes so much faster for me. I asked Ryan to help protect some alone time-space for me when everyone arrived.

A friend came to get Luke and picked up the kids from school for us so that I could concentrate on laboring. As soon as I knew someone was taking care of the kids, I relaxed and knew my labor would be fast. Now I could focus.

I snuck away to my bedroom and took a hot shower. The water is always so relaxing. I bent my knees and would go limp, completely surrendering to every contraction. Then all of a sudden, I felt his head. There was no moving to get anybody this time. He was coming, and he was coming quickly.

I yelled for Ryan, and everyone came into the bathroom in a hurry. My water broke right at that moment. Corrina threw on her gloves and caught Micah just in the nick of time as I was standing there in the shower.

The shower was still going because everything happened so fast. Micah was quite slippery from the water, but Corrina was not about to let him slip out of her hands. Once she had a firm grip on him, she handed him to me. This was my fourth pain-free supernatural birth experience. From the bloody show to Micah being in my arms was five hours.

With all of my births, I had very short pushing periods (just a few minutes.) I never pushed more than two pushes, and even though the babies came out quickly, my perineum remained intact. I never once received a stitch.

# POSTPARTUM TESTIMONY

I experienced great pregnancies and births, but it didn't stop there. Did you ever consider that postpartum can be supernatural as well? I healed quickly and felt fantastic right away. I lost weight efficiently and never dealt with postpartum depression. I had so much joy.

My babies nursed well and had good latches because I asked for help. The first week after Ezekiel's birth, my nipples started to feel sore. I called some breastfeeding experts; they came over and taught me everything I needed to know. It made all the difference. I never had sore nipples again. I nursed four babies without getting cracked or sore nipples or any kind of breast infection.

When Ezekiel was one month old, he seemed uncomfortable and gassy. I called the breastfeeding experts once again and learned about hindmilk and foremilk. I stopped switching breasts during each feed. Instead, I had him feed on one breast only each time. He slept much better and had less gas. I used these tips with all of my babies, and they were very content.

Speak life over yourself and your baby. Don't put down your body. Look at yourself in the mirror and thank your body for creating and birthing life. Embrace all that you are and all that God designed you to be as a mother. Thank your breasts for making the perfect amount of nutritious milk for the baby to thrive. Speak out what you want your body to do, like you will heal quickly without any problems or irritations.

Make declarations such as I have supernatural energy and strength and never grow weary, for I wait on the Lord. I am a good mom. God is pleased with me. I am exactly who my child needs. God chose me to mother this child. I am not alone; God is with me. Where peace dwells, fear cannot. The Prince of Peace dwells within me.

One of the reasons I had such a tremendous postpartum experience is because I asked for help. Postpartum is not the time to be alone. It's when we need community. There is strength in that. There are so many wise moms out there with great experience and tips.

If you need help, ask for it. If you need a good nap, call someone to come over and hold your new baby or take your toddlers out to the park so you can rest. I'm sure they would love it too! Talk to a friend or your church about organizing a meal train for you after you give birth. It's easy to feel overwhelmed and exhausted due to lack of sleep. The smallest gesture can change everything. Let people love you and bless you. We need each other.

# POSTPARTUM TIPS

There are physical ways to prepare for a great postpartum. A woman's blood volume increases about 45% more throughout pregnancy. Iron is necessary for hemoglobin formation, and hemoglobin is required to transport oxygen throughout the body and help the baby. Before labor, a healthy hemoglobin level means less chance of hemorrhage, a better recovery, and the baby will do better during labor.

It isn't unusual for your hemoglobin to drop during pregnancy. It would be best if you aimed for hemoglobin over twelve before labor. Have your levels checked at the twenty-eight-week visit and again at thirty-six. I recommend taking chlorophyll and the supplement Blood Builder by Mega Foods.

The third trimester is the final stretch making it a great time to increase your nutrient intake. Focus on eating vegetables. Make sure you are consuming quality protein daily. Here is a list of proteins other than meat: almonds, hazelnuts, walnuts, pecans, brazil nuts, sunflower seeds, bean sprouts, dates, coconuts, bananas, tomatoes, okra, squash, alfalfa sprouts, quinoa, broccoli, carrots, cabbage, eggplant, hemp seeds, chia seeds, beans, and spirulina.

Increase your good fats from wild-caught seafood (not farm-raised). Use organic coconut oil, avocado oil, or ghee for cooking, and save the organic olive oil for eating raw like in salad dressings. Other good fats include avocados, walnuts, almonds, and flax seeds. Consider limiting dairy intake in the last weeks of your pregnancy because dairy chunks the baby up.

Another way to prepare for postpartum is with physical exercise. Get out and go for a walk for at least 30- 45 minutes, five days a week. Practice squatting also. Squats strengthen your pelvic floor and prepare you for pushing out your baby. Build your way up to 20 squats and holding the squat for 60-90 seconds. You will be happy in the postpartum recovery that you exercised.

A postpartum tip I received before I had my first child was to get a postpartum girdle. I wore the girdle underwear to train my muscles and skin to go back to normal after each birth. I pretty much wore them 24/7 for a couple of months. My stomach got nice and flat again each time. My personal opinion is that it prevents Diastasis Recti (abdominal separation) as well. They worked wonders for me, so I had to share!

# Who Will You Believe?

# CHAPTER 5

God spoke to me, saying I would have children, great pregnancies, and easy labors. On the other hand, the world thinks we will have long, challenging, and painful labors, with possible complications. Pregnancy is awful, miserable, and uncomfortable. You will have all kinds of pains, symptoms, and sicknesses, such as morning sickness, heartburn, sciatica, pelvic pain, and gestational diabetes, to name a few.

When God challenged the way I thought about pregnancy and childbirth, I knew I needed to choose who to believe. The choice was to believe God at His Word or what people say about pregnancy and childbirth. In my case, I decided to believe God and activated my faith around the subject.

The definition of belief is an acceptance that a statement is true or that something exists. It is trust, faith, or confidence in someone or something. Belief is a state or habit of mind in which trust and confidence are placed in a person or thing. It is a conviction of the truth. What state of mind do you have when it comes to pregnancy and childbirth? In whom or what do you place your trust and confidence?

I'm glad you got a glimpse of my faith in action with my testimony. I know many think everything was easy for me when they hear I had pain-free births, but they don't realize all the trials and choices I made along the way. Everything was not "easy" for me on this journey. Don't be deceived into thinking that when you get a promise, it's all going to be rainbows. Opposition comes to the Word. It comes with a purpose to steal the Kingdom and God's thoughts from being sown in your heart. If the Word remains no matter what, you will bear fruit. The parable of the sower reveals this to us.

Right now, a word from the Lord is being sown into your heart. Will you allow the enemy to steal what God is speaking to you? You can have children easily and without pain! Do you believe it? You choose and decide whether to accept it or not?

What you choose to believe is true for you. For instance, if you think life is hard, you will experience a lot of hardship. If you believe that God doesn't heal today, you won't partner with Him for healing. If you believe that childbirth is painful, you will have what you believe.

What are you believing? Are you going to believe what the world system feeds you, or do you believe that all things are possible with God? God didn't just speak this to me. He is saying this to you now also! I understand there are a lot of women who have had a bad experience. That is a reality, but there is another reality. You must make a conscious decision as to what mindset you want. Dr. Caroline Leaf (a neuroscientist) states, whatever choice you make will become a physical substance in your brain.

"Now faith is the substance of things hoped for, the evidence of things not seen." - Hebrews 11:1

Faith is a physical substance in your brain. Are you having substance in the enemy camp, or is your substance in God's Word? What are you patterning yourself after? The Bible warns us not to conform to this world's patterns but to be transformed by renewing our minds. Did you know that ninety-nine percent of how you perceive things comes from what you have built in your brain? What you choose to believe about pregnancy and childbirth wires your brain to perceive it a certain way.

How have you wired your brain about childbirth? Have you wired it to believe in pain, stress, fear, sickness, complications, and anxiety? I know I did before God broke through into my thinking. The good news is that you are never stuck. You can renew old patterns of thinking by feasting on the truth until your thoughts and actions became one with the Spirit of God. It is not hard to do since we have the mind of Christ. Sit, feast, and allow the transformation to happen.

# The Curse

Where did the pain in childbirth originate? Does it have its origin in God? Let's feast on the Word together to better understand the story of Adam and Eve, the curse, what that brought, and God's plan of redemption. It is vital to fully grasp what this story contains because it holds keys to unlocking the Kingdom into womanhood, childbirth, and motherhood.

For many years I perceived the story of the fall as a source of condemnation. It once represented the beginning of punishment and banishment to me. I saw God as a harsh God. I know I am not the only one who has ever felt that way. Today I see it completely different through the renewing of my mind and revelation. I now see it as the beginning of the most extraordinary love story ever told. In the middle of humanity's darkest hour, the God of love stepped into our situation. He never condemned us, nor left us, once. It has never been His heart to see us perish or remain separated from Him, so He devised a perfect plan. A plan that could not be thwarted. A plan that reconciled us to Him forever.

Adam and Eve's story is well known and easily overlooked for the power and redemption these few verses hold. I want you to read their story with fresh eyes and a heart open to what the Holy Spirit wants to reveal to you. Let's start at the beginning.

God created both male and female in the image of the Father, Son, and Holy Spirit, for He said, "Let Us make man in Our image, according to Our likeness." He also gave them complete authority over the entire earth and all the animals. He blessed them and said, *"Be fruitful, multiply, fill the earth and subdue it (putting it under your power), and rule over the fish of the sea, the birds of the air, and every living thing that moves upon the earth."*

He told Adam that He had given them every plant and tree for food also. They could eat freely from every tree of the garden except the tree of the knowledge of good and evil. They were not to eat from it; otherwise, they would die. God hid nothing from them. He was upfront and honest. He even told Adam that the tree contained the knowledge of good and evil.

One day, the serpent came to the woman and planted doubt in her mind by challenging what God had said. He mixed lies with the truth. There is a truth in the statement that eating the fruit would open their eyes to know both good and evil. However, this knowledge will not be a blessing, as the devil makes it seem.

He lies by telling the woman she would certainly not die if she ate the fruit but would be like God. This statement implied that something was missing or God was withholding something.

In essence, the serpent wanted her to believe that she needed to do something to become what she already was. God had already created man and woman in His image according to His likeness. She was already like God.

The devil still uses these tactics today. He lures us to step outside of God to try to attain the things of God. He whispers, "If you do this, you will have this." God says, "You have this, trust me."

The problem started when Eve let the serpent rule over her instead of her ruling over it. God gave her authority and power to rule over every living thing that moves upon the earth, including the serpent. Instead, she inclined her ear towards him and allowed him the privilege to speak into her life.

She questioned what God said but did not question what the serpent spoke. She chose to listen to the wrong voice. She thought about what the serpent said, looked at the tree, saw that it was good for food, pleasant to look at, and desired to eat it to make her wise. She ate it, thinking it would make her wise, but she didn't gain wisdom; she gained knowledge. She chose the fruit of works. Everything that was once hers through rest, now was hers through hard work and toil. The fruit she ate was not life-giving, but a fruit unto death, for you cannot receive life abundantly through human effort.

Once the fruit opened their eyes, they realized their condition. They were naked and uncovered. They came out from God's covering and tried to cover themselves through their works. They made clothes out of leaves with their own hands. Then God shows up. He calls out to them as they are hiding in shame and full of fear. Where are you?

As a mom, can't you hear the sadness in His voice, knowing His children are lost eternally at this moment? The separation was real; where are you? Notice that God doesn't hide from them, cast them out of His presence, or turn His face from sin. On the contrary, He sets out to find them and come to their rescue as a good Father does. He talks to them face to face, corruption and all. I pray you can comprehend the great magnitude of God's wondrous love in all its dimensions and that you see how deeply intimate and far-reaching His love is as you read this!

When God gets to them, He asks if they ate from the tree He commanded them they should not eat. A quarrel breaks out among the parties involved. They all start pointing fingers. Then the most amazing thing happens, just when they lost all hope.

God took up the quarrel personally and disgraced the serpent on the battlefield upon which he had gained temporary success. This fight will not be between the serpent and man but between the serpent and God Himself. When you feel taken advantage of, deceived, and at a considerable loss, nothing brings more comfort than a righteous protector and judge who fights for you.

When the enemy comes in, like a flood, the Spirit of the Lord will lift up a standard against him. At this moment, God raises a standard. He turns to the serpent and starts with this statement.

The Lord God said to the serpent,

*"Because you have done this, You are cursed more than all the cattle, And more than any animal of the field; On your belly, you shall go, And dust you shall eat All the days of your life. "And I will put enmity (open hostility) Between you and the woman, And between your seed and her Seed; He shall bruise your head, And you shall bruise His heel." Genesis 3:14-15*

This scripture clearly states that the serpent is cursed. "Because you have done this, You are cursed." God continues by declaring the promise of our Savior within this same breath. It is the first gospel sermon delivered upon the surface of the earth. Jehovah Himself is the preacher, and the whole human race and the prince of darkness are His audience. He declares at this moment that the serpent is defeated and it will come through the woman.

It must have pleased God to announce to the serpent that the woman's Seed should bruise his head. In the worst sense, the serpent destroyed a part of God's creation by introducing sin into the world. The serpent stamped the human race with his image and gained new forces to promote rebellion and sin. I'm sure he felt so smug and powerful looking at what he had accomplished by deceiving the woman.

Satan made a grand scheme and thought that he had won the moment Adam and Eve fell. He figured all of man's descendants would now forever be under his rule and dominion. He may have felt a sense of victory, but it didn't last. God raises a standard and declares, "I will put enmity between you and the woman, between your seed and her Seed; He shall bruise your head, and you shall bruise his heel." He promised a champion would arise at that moment, and even though He would suffer, He would win and leave a mortal wound to the serpent's head.

The serpents victory dance subsided when he realized his demise was imminent. His hatred for women and the birth of new life burned within him. I'm not sure how much Adam and Eve understood about this prophecy at the time, but they must have found some comfort in these words. Their seed would be victorious over the instigator of their ruin.

The start of rival kingdoms had begun. There is enmity between Christ and satan because He came to destroy the devil's works and set free all oppressed and under bondage. For this purpose, Jesus was born. For this purpose, He lived, He died, was resurrected, seated at the Father's right hand, and will come again.

Jesus is the prophetic Word spoken of at the fall of mankind that would champion this cause and oppose satan. The enmity between the seeds continues as we preach Christ crucified. Every sermon shakes the gates of hell. We overcome the evil one through the blood of the Lamb and the Word of our testimony.

Childbirth is the vehicle God used to bring this promise into being. When sin entered the world, childbirth became different. God's original design for birth was free from pain, sorrow, and toil.

The fall ushered in the curse, fear, death, pain, sickness, to name a few. These things do not have their origin in God. It came from partnering with something outside of Him. God, in His great mercy, devised a sacrificial plan to restore all that was lost.

Even though Eve was deceived and fell into transgression, bringing sorrow, toil, and pain into conception and childbirth, God redeemed us all. *"Nevertheless, she will be <u>saved</u> in childbearing if they continue in faith, love, and holiness, with self-control." Timothy 2:15.* The word <u>saved</u> here is sozo. Sozo means to save, heal, preserve, deliver and rescue. Jesus entered the world through means of childbirth to save, heal, and rescue us. He redeemed us! The curse is broken.

Now remain in faith, agape love, and holiness (set apart) with self-control. The word "with" here is *meta*, which means a change afterward or what results after the activity. The word self-control is *sophrosune*, which means soundness of mind. You could read it as "remain in faith, agape love, and holiness, and the change you see from remaining in these things results in a sound mind."

Women, we have been rescued. We are whole emotionally and physically. We have a sound mind. The healing is here. Step into your Sozo.

# Did God Curse Adam and Eve?

The *Rhema* Word from Jehovah released hope and *dunamis* power to Adam and Eve before they even heard the consequences of their actions. After God spoke to the serpent and preached the first gospel message, He turned to the woman and said: *"I will greatly multiply your sorrow and your conception; In pain, you shall bring forth children; Your desire shall be for your husband, And he shall rule over you." Genesis 3:16*

I want you to note that God did not say cursed are you to the woman. Women were not cursed. However, eating the fruit that carried the curse brought that fruit into our lives. The original word used for sorrow and pain in this text is the word "atsab." The definition is pain, toil, sorrow, and hardship. This same word is also used when speaking to Adam when He says in sorrow and toil you shall eat.

I find this interesting because when you think of a man eating the fruit of his labor, you don't picture him writhing in pain. No, he isn't literally in physical pain while he is eating his food. Did he toil for it? Was it hard work? Were there difficulties? Was there some sorrow and anguish along the way? That's what you think of when grasping what God is talking about here towards Adam.

Why do we see it differently when looking at it in regards to childbirth? When the curse came into being, pregnancy and conception were now going to be hard work. The hard work of it all was now multiplied. The work brings with it sorrow, toil, labor, and pain, both physically and emotionally. In this kind of pain, we would bring forth children.

After God speaks to the woman, He directs His conversation now to Adam, saying,

*"Because you have listened to the voice of your wife, and have eaten [fruit] from the tree about which I commanded you, saying, 'You shall not eat of it';*
*The ground is [now] under a curse because of you; In sorrow and toil, you shall eat [the fruit] of it all the days of your life.*

*"Both thorns and thistles it shall grow for you, And you shall eat the plants of the field.*
*"By the sweat of your face You will eat bread until you re-turn to the ground, For from it you were taken; For you are dust, And to dust, you shall return."*
*Genesis 3:17-19*

God never states that He cursed Adam. He said that the ground is now under a curse because of what you have done. The word curse is used twice in these scriptures, but it never was mentioned that God cursed Adam and Eve. Their choices brought them under the curse. God can not curse what he has blessed. That means He has gone back on His Word, which He can't do. Psalm 138:2 says that You have magnified Your Word above all Your name.

The story of Balak and Balaam shows us that no one can curse what God has blessed. Balak asks Balaam to come and curse the children of Israel. Balaam responds to Balak by saying, *"God is not a man that He should lie, Nor a son of man, that He should repent. Has he said, and will He not do? Or has He spoken, and will He not make it good? Behold, I have received a command to bless: He has blessed, and I cannot reverse it." Numbers 23:19-20* Balaam understood he couldn't speak a curse over the people.

He could not reverse the Lord's blessing through his words because the words of man are not higher than God's. The only way to curse them was by enticing them to sin. Proverbs chapter twenty-six verse two says, *"as the bird by wandering, as the swallow by flying, so the curse causeless shall not come."*

We are blessed and not cursed! We should not walk with sin, death, and curse consciousness, but a righteousness and blessing consciousness. As a new creation, we need to renew our minds to the truth that God's word over us is a blessing and walk in it. No one can reverse this blessing. God's Word is final, and the Word took on all the effects of the curse on the cross and said, "It is finished." The curse died with Jesus. It is buried and has no place in those who have made themselves alive to Christ.

# The Blessing

In the beginning, God blessed man and woman telling them to be fruitful, multiply, fill the earth and subdue it. That is God's will, and it hasn't changed, for He changes not. Blessing is God's nature, so incline your ear to truth and do what God says. Deuteronomy 28 says that if you pay attention to the Lord your God's voice and do what He says, all these blessings will come upon you:

You will be blessed in the city (in your community).

You will be blessed in the field (wherever you work).

Your children will be blessed and the fruit of your womb.

Your land and food will be blessed.

Your animals will be blessed.

He will bless your baskets and pans and fill them with food.

He will bless you at all times in everything that you do.

When you come in and when you go out.

When enemies come to fight against you, He will make your

enemies run away from you in seven different ways.

God will command the blessing upon you in your storehouses (your savings, that which you are storing up).

He will bless everything you do.

The Lord will make you rich.

You will lend and not borrow.

You will be the head and not the tail, on top and not the bottom.

The list of blessings here is beautiful. Through Jesus, we are the head and not the tail. When Jesus bruised the serpent's head, we regained our authority. Satan is no longer the head, but Christ is the church's head, which is His seed. We are on top, no longer under bondage. Satan is under our feet. The picture of Christ bruising the serpent's head and then the serpent bruising Christ's heel shows us the reversal of roles. It is finished!

Without God, we would be lost and forever under the dominion of sorrow, pain, sickness, toil, death, and so on. The book of Proverbs chapter ten verse twenty-two says, *"The blessing of the Lord makes one rich, and He adds no sorrow with it."* This word sorrow is the same word *"atsab"* found stated when the curse entered into the world. The good news is that the blessing of the Lord is void of that kind of fruit, for He is life.

Jesus is the answer. He is our champion! The one who crushed Satan under his feet and defeated sin and death. Through Jesus, we have a better covenant established on better promises.

*Hebrews 8:6*
*"But now He (Jesus) has obtained a more excellent ministry, inasmuch as He is also Mediator of a better covenant, which was*

*established on better promises."*

# The Woman Is Named

After God's discourse to the serpent, the woman, and Adam, Adam did something profound. Sometimes it's the simple things we do that show where our faith lies. Adam acted immediately in faith in what God had said, for faith comes by hearing and hearing the Word of God. *"And Adam called his wife's name Eve because she was the mother of all the living," Genesis 3:20.* Before the fall, she was known only as woman. Adam prophetically named his wife Eve because it means life. In the natural, she was not a mother at all. However, life was to come through her by the promised Seed.

There stood Adam, freshly stained from sins grip, and he turns to his fellow culprit, who was probably trembling too, and he calls her Eve, mother of the life that is yet to be. God didn't leave them hopeless and defined by death. He didn't label the woman as the bringer of death. On the contrary, He proclaimed that through woman's Seed would come life and redemption.

Adam's faith in the new promise gave him hope. He released that hope to his wife by giving her a new identity. He named her Eve (life). What a great husband. He made sure she was known as the woman who brings forth life instead of bringing death. Adam had the privilege of naming every creature God made. Whatever he called them, that was its name. Adam naming Eve was a defining moment. He made a stand to partner with God and proclaimed the promise from that day forward. The name Eve was intentional.

God heard what Adam named his wife and knew he was a believer in the promise. Right away, God made Adam and Eve clothes of skin. An animal died through shed blood to become a covering, which foreshadows perfect righteousness. This righteousness can only come through the shedding of blood. Jesus has delivered us from the serpent's power by covering us with His righteousness by shedding His blood. Love covers a multitude of sins, and His mercy endures forever. For God so loved the world that He gave His only begotten Son, that whosoever believes in Him should not perish but have everlasting life.

# Redeemed From the Curse

Adam and Eve's story is not a story of doom and gloom but of mercy, the promise of a Savior, victory, and God's great love. The curse is not the end of the story but rather just the beginning. It is a perfect example of how God turns everything around for our good. God's plan turns ruin into redemption and the curse into a blessing. There is only one way for us to be delivered from the curse and to experience the blessing of God's cure. It is through faith in Jesus, the promised messiah. He bore the curse.

Galatians 3:13-14, 29 says, *"Christ has redeemed us from the curse of the law, having become a curse for us (for it is written, "cursed is everyone who hangs on a tree"), that the blessing of Abraham might come upon the Gentiles in Christ Jesus, that we might receive the promise of the Spirit through faith. And if you are Christ's, then you are Abraham's seed, and heirs according to the promise."*

All those who are in Christ by faith are delivered from the curse and delight in the cure. Those who reject Christ remain in Adam, under the curse. We have been redeemed, so the blessing of Abraham could come upon us. If we have received the blessing of Abraham through Christ Jesus, what does that include? Gen. 24:1 says, *"Now Abraham was old, well advanced in age, and the Lord had blessed Abraham in ALL things."* ALL things cover every aspect of our life like pregnancy, conception, supernatural childbirth, health, wisdom, parenting, increase, a great marriage, physical provisions, peace, wealth, talking with God, intimacy with God, and faith. Grab ahold of this truth by faith!! Your inheritance in Christ Jesus is to be blessed in ALL things!

Another powerful truth is that we have been redeemed from the curse, including painful childbirth. The word redeemed means to rescue from captivity or bondage or from any obligation or liability to suffer by making atonement. It also means to recover or regain possession of, to save, and to deliver. It is vital to know all that we have been saved from and everything recovered for our benefit.

# Jesus Has Carried Our Pains

*Isaiah 53:4*

*Surely He has borne our griefs and carried our sorrows.*

The Hebrew word for grief here is Choli which means sickness. The Hebrew word for sorrows here is Makob which means pains (both physical and mental). I like the Youngs Literal Translation of this verse because it puts it in perspective for me.

*Isaiah 53:4 (YLT)*

*Surely our sickness He hath borne, and our pains—*
*He hath carried them.*

Most Christians believe that Jesus bore our sicknesses, and by His stripes, we are healed but haven't understood that He carried our pains too. The bondage of pain is not my master, but Christ who carried pain away. Jesus triumphed over sickness and pain, so now I can too!

That doesn't mean that we won't have trials in this life. On earth, we have an adversary that wants to steal, kill, and destroy. Jesus said, "In the world, you will have tribulation; but be of good cheer, I have overcome the world." John 16:33. Rest in the finished work of Christ and be of good cheer. Victory is yours!

# Jesus Has Loosed Us From Pain

On the day of Pentecost, everyone in the upper room was filled with the Holy Spirit and tongues of fire. Then Peter preaches boldly to the crowd. In this sermon prompted by the Holy Spirit, he delivers this revelation that I hope every woman can grasp.

*"Him (Jesus), being delivered by the determined purpose and foreknowledge of God, you have taken by lawless hands, have crucified, and put to death; whom God raised up, having loosed the pains of death because it was not possible that He should be held by it."*
*Acts 2:23-24*

The word pains used here is the word "*odin*," which means a birth pang, the pain of childbirth. Jesus loosed the pains of childbirth and all pains of death when he rose from the grave.

He could not be held by it, and neither are we. Jesus is the firstborn over all creation. He is the beginning, the firstborn from the dead, that He may have preeminence in all things. Jesus was the last Adam who redeemed everything the first Adam brought upon us. He overcame the world, the flesh, death, and the devil. He is seated at the Father's right hand in triumph, and we are seated with Him in heavenly places.

When we get the revelation of our position in Christ, we will enjoy the rights and privileges that already belong to us as joint-heirs. We will no longer act as defeated women but will take our place as triumphant women, which was God's design from the world's foundation.

Jesus reconciled ALL things. He didn't leave one thing out. He recovered everything through the blood of His cross. *"It pleased the Father that in Him all the fullness should dwell, and by Him to reconcile all things to Himself, by Him, whether things on earth or in heaven, having made peace through the blood of His cross (Colossians 1:19)."*

**A list of some of the things Jesus won back for us through His blood is as follows:**

+ The curse came in with sin, so Christ was made a curse for us.

+ We were bound by the pains of death and painful childbirth (physical pain), so Jesus loosed us from them.

+ Sorrow (mental pain) came in with sin, so Jesus carried our sorrows.

+ We were lost and going astray, so the Lord laid on Jesus the iniquity of us all.

+ Sickness came in with sin, so He took them on, and by His stripes, we are healed.

+ Thorns came in with sin, so He was crowned with thorns for us.

✝ Jesus was pierced in his side, restoring women to their rightful place (the woman was taken from Adam's side). The piercing on the side is also a representation of the Bride of Christ coming forth from Jesus, perfect, beautiful, and pure.

✝ Sweat and toil came in with sin, so He sweat drops of blood for us.

✝ Death and disobedience came in with sin, so He became obedient unto death and then rose again!

The chapter of Isaiah fifty-three starts with a question. "Who has believed our report? And to whom has the arm of the Lord been revealed?" Then Isaiah prophecies of Jesus' coming, death and resurrection 700 years before Jesus even appeared in the flesh on this earth.

Everything Jesus endured on the cross was the fulfillment of the prophecy given by Jehovah at the fall of mankind. As stated earlier, for this prophecy to come to pass, satan would bruise Jesus' heel.

Isaiah prophesied, "He was wounded for our transgressions, He was bruised for our iniquities; the chastisement for our peace was upon Him, and by His stripes, we are healed." From the very beginning, Jehovah Himself declared this would take place and that this act would be our victory. Isaiah also prophesies this, saying, *"Yet it pleased the Lord to bruise Him; He has put Him to grief. When You make His soul an offering for sin, He shall see His seed, He shall prolong His days, And the pleasure of the Lord shall prosper in His hand. He shall see the labor of His soul and be satisfied. By His knowledge, My righteous Servant shall justify many, For He shall bear their iniquities."* *Isaiah 53:10-11*

Did you catch that? These verses contain the words *bruise* and *seed*. These are the same words used by Jehova Himself at the beginning. *When You make His soul an offering for sin, He shall see His seed!* When Jesus hung on the cross, He saw you and me, but not in our sin. He could see us in Him, righteous, perfect, and set free!

The joy that was set before Him was us, His seed. Through Him, many will be justified. Jesus is the first fruit of this new seed, which conquers sin and death through His righteousness. The knowledge of good and evil brought death to humanity, but Jesus justified many by His knowledge and bearing our sins. Fix your eyes on Jesus, the author and finisher of our faith. Christ, whom we serve, is more able to save than satan is to destroy.

By His sufferings, Jesus has overthrown satan. Satan intended to make humankind the captives of his power and thought that this world would be the arena of his victory over God and good. Instead, we have been redeemed from this yoke of slavery to sin and death. We have been crucified with Christ. We are born again, a new creation with eternal life, seated with Christ in triumph in heavenly places. Thus satan's plans have been foiled. It's time to shout with a voice of triumph, "Oh death, where is your sting? O grave, where is your victory?" Believe the report of the Lord!

# Conceiving & Birthing The Supernatural

# CHAPTER 6

If you are having trouble getting pregnant or were told that you couldn't have children, it's time to conceive the supernatural!! You can apply this chapter to any blockages you are experiencing, not just infertility.

How do we conceive the supernatural and then see it manifest in our lives when things are blocked or aren't working in the natural? First, it is crucial to believe the report of the Lord. Jesus came, He is the Son of God, died for our sins, and was resurrected. We are healed and have been made whole. He became a curse for us, so we are no longer under the curse. He broke every curse over our life. We are now the righteousness of Christ Jesus and share in His inheritance. Knowing this report and believing it, let us look at what Isaiah says after the prophetic word of redemption.

Isaiah 54 starts immediately with *"Sing, O Barren."* The good news of what we have in Christ should make us want to rejoice. Our response to such fantastic news is praise and worship.

"Sing, O barren,

You who have not borne!

Break forth into singing, and cry aloud,

You who have not labored with child!

For more are the children of the desolate

Than the children of the married woman," says the Lord.


"Do not fear for you will not be ashamed;

Neither be disgraced, for you will not be put to shame;

For you will forget the shame of your youth,

And will not remember the reproach of your widowhood anymore."


The woman described here has two strikes against her. First, she can not physically conceive because she is barren. Second, she is a widow and has no husband. In other words, it is double impossible for this woman to have a child.

Maybe you feel like this woman. Not only do you think this is impossible, but you feel like all the odds are stacked against you. Well, it's time to hear the voice of God over your circumstance. You who think this is entirely impossible, it's time to SING!!! It's time to start rejoicing and getting excited!! Why? Based on what? God says SING for MORE are the children of the desolate than the children of the married woman. With God on your side, you will have better results than those who have a natural way to get things done. How can this be?

Let us continue reading the passage.

"For your Maker is your husband,

The Lord of hosts is His name

And your Redeemer is the Holy One of Israel;

He is called the God of the whole earth."

You will have better results for your Maker is your husband! The Great I AM says I will step into the place where there are a gap and lack. Where nothing seems to be working for you and all odds are stacked against you, I'm bringing My ability and My power into your situation. I am your husband, and with Me, you will conceive the supernatural in your life. The impossibilities will become possible. I am the God of the impossible, and the supernatural produces better results than the natural.

This truth should excite you so much that you start celebrating right now!!! SING O barren one.

My husband Ryan, although amazing, has limited resources and abilities in and of himself. If my trust relies on what I have in the natural and what I see, I will be limited. I will reap the natural in my life. However, if I take my eyes off the natural by putting my trust in God and making Him my source and my husband, I will step into the supernatural. This realm has unlimited resources. God has capabilities that go beyond what we can naturally do or accomplish in our strength. Psalm 118:8 says it best. *"It is better to trust in the Lord than to put confidence in man."* To whom are you placing your trust and confidence in this situation?

The enemy wants us to remain in the realm of sight and be led by our feelings and emotions. He does not want us to have an abundant life or to step into the supernatural. His goal is not only to keep us in the realm of the natural, but to steal, kill, and destroy there as well.

We walk by faith and not by sight. The enemy does not want

us in the faith zone. He wants us to be motivated by fear and lack. God says very plainly to this situation, "Do not fear for you will not be ashamed; neither be disgraced, for you will not be put to shame."

God knows the enemy's tactics and reassures us not to fear because He will come through for us. Shame has no place in this situation. Fear and shame are outside of God and His blessing. Don't partner with anything outside of Him. We know where that leads us.

When God speaks His prophetic words and promises to us, it is up to us to believe and receive them. To see the promises manifest in the natural, we need to conceive them in the spirit first. "Now faith is the substance of things hoped for, the evidence of things not seen. For by it, the elders obtained a good testimony." Hebrews chapter 11 says that the elders obtained a good testimony by faith. Their faith in God birthed the supernatural in their life. We still read about their lives today. We read their struggles and their victories, which gives us all hope. We read the promises fulfilled and celebrate the wins with them. It is by faith that they obtained a good testimony!!

Sarah is a barren woman in the Bible that by faith, obtained a good testimony. She is one of the heroes of faith, and this is what the Bible says about her. *"By faith, Sarah herself also received strength to conceive seed, and she bore a child when she was past the age because she judged Him faithful who had promised. Therefore from one man, and him as good as dead, were born as many as the stars of the sky in multitude—innumerable as the sand which is by the seashore."* Hebrews 11:11-12

Sarah was 90 years old when she finally gets pregnant, and Abraham was 99. Not only does it say that she was past the age of childbearing, but her husband was as good as dead. That statement makes me laugh. When it comes to Abraham at this age, nothing is working down there anymore. It sounds like his sperm was no longer alive and active. We all know through their story that Sarah was barren. Abraham was not the cause of her inability to get pregnant, and everyone knew it when Hagar conceived. Everything was working just fine for Abraham. Although, by the time they finally conceived Isaac, it says that Abraham was as good as dead. He was infertile now too.

Then there was Sarah. Not only was she barren, but she was past her childbearing age. Menopause came and went. The odds were stacked against Abraham and Sarah. It was no longer a little impossible; this was utterly impossible. Science would test this couple and, say, start looking at ways to adopt. There is no way you will ever conceive a child. The natural realm has a voice and speaks what it sees. God has a voice, and He says what He sees. He calls what isn't into being.

How did Sarah birth the supernatural in her life? I want to point out a few keys found in scripture about her. The first thing is she took full responsibility. It says by faith Sarah herself. Nobody could do this for her. She could not ride on the curtain tails of her husband's faith or anyone else's, for that matter. She had to do this herself. The same is true for us. Take responsibility.

There is another key that will help us unlock the supernatural in our lives found in these verses. "By faith, Sarah herself also received strength to conceive seed, and she bore a child when she was past the age because she judged Him faithful who had promised." Notice it says "SHE" and not because of God. It doesn't say that she conceived because God promised. It also doesn't say that she conceived because it was the will of God. It says by faith Sarah HERSELF RECEIVED strength to conceive and bear a child because SHE judged Him faithful who had promised.

God spoke to Sarah and promised she would have a child. You

O Barren One, you will have a child! You are going to have so many children through that child it is going to be innumerable.

The promise of God over Sarah's life was a seed that was sown. Sarah needed to receive it by faith to conceive it. She didn't judge the promises of God or the validity of the promise. She judged God Himself and made up her mind that God was faithful. She decided every promise He spoke over her; He would make them come to pass despite every natural barrier and block.

It no longer mattered how old she was, how barren she was, if she produced eggs anymore, or even if her husband was infertile now too. She knew that together with God, they would overcome all of this because He promised, and I'm judging Him faithful!! We can learn a lot from Sarah. We must conceive the promises of God by faith and judge Him faithful who promises!! When God speaks, receive it. Meditate on His promises, declare them over your life, and SING O Barren One.

That all sounds great, but you don't understand my situation. There is no way I can get pregnant. The doctors have confirmed it. I keep miscarrying; it is not meant to be for me. I've had abortions, I don't deserve to have children, and the list can go on and on. It doesn't matter what your circumstances are or what you have done in your past. God is speaking His promises over your life. You don't need evidence.

Do you know who is talking to you? Do you know who is announcing this message to you? I Am that I Am, and if I tell you that you will have children, you will have children. Receive it and believe it. If you do not receive the seed, you will not conceive it.

It's time to tune into the voice of God over your life instead of your shame, disappointment, fears, and your worries. There is healing, life, and truth in His words. Receive and conceive what God says over you. Let the truth of His words smash every lie that would try to take residence in your mind. God is for you.

There is no condemnation for those who are in Christ. Our mistakes do not nullify the promises of God. God spoke the promise to Sarah, and for many years she didn't conceive it. She got discouraged, just like many of us have along the way. She began to think that there must be another way and therefore came up with a plan. She gave Hagar to Abraham.

She turned to other things and other means as her source to bring about the promise. She didn't judge God faithful at this point yet. She took the matter into her own hands. I don't know about you, but this story releases so much hope to me and is so redemptive. I'm not the only one who struggles and gets discouraged. I'm not the only one who has thought I have waited patiently only to lay down a promise and try to speed it up by my strength and agendas. And yet, God is faithful!! Not only that, Sarah is listed as one of the heroes of faith in Hebrews chapter eleven.

Even one year before Abraham and Sarah had Isaac, they hadn't entirely conceived the promise. When he was 99 years old, God came to Abraham and announced to Him again that He would give him a son through his wife, Sarah. Abraham fell on his face and laughed.

Picture that for a moment. God came to Abraham, delivered a message, and Abraham fell to the ground in laughter. While he is hysterically laughing at what God said, in his heart, he is saying to himself, "Shall a child be born to a man who is 100 years old? And shall Sarah, who is 90 years old, bear a child?" Abraham then told God, Oh, that Ishmael might live before you! God answered, no, Sarah, your wife shall bear a son, and you are to name him Isaac. Isaac means he laughs. Again this is one year before they had Isaac.

After this encounter, the Lord appears to Abraham again by the terebinth trees. Abraham goes into the tent to Sarah and asks her to make cakes. Abraham took all the food and set it before them. Then they said to him, "where is Sarah, your wife?" Abraham answers, "in the tent." He says aloud so Sarah can hear that I will return to you about this time next year and your wife Sarah will have a son.

Sarah was listening at the tent door and laughed within herself, saying, "After I have grown old, shall I have pleasure, my lord being old also?" This thought got God's attention. He stopped and asked Abraham why Sarah laughed. Sarah's reply was precisely the same reply her husband had when he heard it for the first time. Maybe this is why the Lord made sure he announced this news in the hearing of Sarah.

It seems like maybe Abraham didn't share this great news with his wife. It is as if this is new information to her, and she responded by laughing within herself. I believe Sarah got embarrassed when she got put on the spot. She said, oh no, I didn't laugh. But God said, yes, you did laugh.

Sarah's response wasn't breaking forth into singing. She laughed at the promise of God in her heart. God didn't respond by saying, that's it, you don't believe. Your laughing at me, so I'm done working with you. I'm moving on and giving the promise to someone else. God was determined to convince her.

He reminds her, "Is anything too hard for the Lord?" He declares I will be back about this time next year, and Sarah, you will have a son!! God is saying I can make this come to pass. I'm waiting for you to conceive that reality. The words I have spoken to you are enough. Do you believe that? God's words are powerful enough to change every circumstance. God is announcing to you that the supernatural will happen in your life. Will you believe Me because I said it?

These *rhema* words from God stirred Sarah's faith. His question hit straight to the heart of the matter. Is anything too hard for the Lord? He's inviting her to judge Him. She ponders these words in her heart. She realizes she is down to nothing but the promise, and she decided to judge Him faithful who promised!! By faith, Sarah herself also received strength to conceive seed. Dunamis is the word used here for strength. It means miraculous power, and it is a part of God's very nature. No *rhema* word that comes into your heart and is received is without miraculous power.

1 John 15:7
If you abide in Me, and my words (*rhema*) abide in you, you will ask what you desire, and it shall be done for you.

God never leaves us nor forsakes us. He never gives up on us. He wants to convince you how good He truly is so that you will judge Him faithful. We aren't waiting on God to finally do something or come through for us. He is waiting for us. Dare to let go of every excuse by wholeheartedly believing the promises over your life, and judge God faithful.

## Prayer For Conception

Abba Father, I come boldly to the throne of grace, the throne of your gracious favor, with confidence and without fear. I refuse to be anxious. I refuse to worry about anything, but in everything, by prayer and supplication with thanksgiving and with a thankful heart, I make my requests known to you.

I thank you, Father, that my body, which you made, to carry life is perfect. I thank you that my reproductive organs function perfectly in Jesus' name. The blessing you spoke over your creation (man and woman) at the beginning was to be fruitful and to multiply.

My desire is You, O Lord. My heart desires children because you put that desire there when you blessed mankind to be fruitful and multiply. Your Word says that "My Word that goes out from My mouth: it will not return to Me empty or void, but it will accomplish all I want it to, and it will prosper everywhere I send it."

Thank you, Abba Father, that my womb prospers and will bring forth children. Your blessings are not an empty promise. Your words don't fail. They do everything you send it to do.

Body, I command you to come under the authority of God's will, His plans, and His purposes in Jesus' name!! Ovaries, I bless you. You will release an egg every month. Body, I declare that you will secrete progesterone's perfect amount to help prepare the endometrium for the embryo to implant. I am fertile, and my husband is fertile.

I commit my ways to You, and I trust you with my whole heart, knowing You will do it. You will give me the desires of my heart as I delight in You. I choose to delight in You, to be completely satisfied in You. For You satisfy the longing soul, and the hungry soul You fill with good things. I choose as an act of my free will to rest and wait patiently for You. Mind, I command you to be at peace and receive the blessing of the Lord!

In Jesus' name AMEN

# I Birth Fearless

# CHAPTER 7

J ust imagine if the typical conversation about pregnancy and birth went more like this; "Oh, you are pregnant! Congratulations! Pregnancy was the most wonderful experience of my life. I felt fantastic my whole pregnancy and loved every minute of it. All my labors were fast and easy, without any complications. I can't even explain the joy and strength I felt. It is one of the most empowering moments as a woman. You are going to have a great pregnancy and birth. There is so much to look forward to." That is what I say when starting a conversation with someone pregnant, and they seem relieved every time. I can see hope surge through their bodies, and they always lean in to hear more. They are entirely open to any wisdom that I carry, even if it contains the gospel of Jesus Christ.

Many fears are associated with pregnancy and childbirth, mainly because we are taught to fear it. People pass down their labor stories fueled with fear and negativity, such as how painful it was, what went wrong, how it turned into an emergency, and so on.

It is far easier to hear all the bad stories than to find anyone talking about how wonderful it is and how everything was easy, without any complications. We get saturated in all the bad news about pregnancy and childbirth. We hear it in media, see it in shows and movies, and get it when talking to loved ones and friends. My heart is to see kingdom women flip this script through the power of God working in and through us.

It is crucial to deal with every fear associated with pregnancy and childbirth because fear directly affects how you birth your children. When you are afraid or feeling uncomfortable during your labor, it will cause you to tense up. Fear is a spirit that doesn't come from God.

Fear is the response to a real or imagined perception of danger. It comes with physical symptoms such as rapid heart rate and muscle tension, especially in the abdomen. When you tense up, you work against your contractions. Your mind and your body are now in conflict with one another.

Your body is designed to birth with ease, but when fear enters, your mind sends signals that fight what your body is trying to accomplish. Your brain is the body's control center. It sends messages to your body through a network of nerves called "the nervous system," which controls your muscles. The uterus is the strongest muscle in your body. The uterus's pressure and power in labor are the strongest force exerted by any muscle in the body. God designed us perfectly to birth children. Women's bodies are extraordinary.

Pain in labor can enter through fear. In the early 1900s, two obstetricians—Dr. Jonathan Dye and Dr. Grantley Dick Read—were researching why the poorer, less educated patients experienced better births with significantly less pain and complications than their more affluent counterparts. They concluded that the poorer women did not have as much fear around labor and delivery, which resulted in better experiences and healthier outcomes. This study realized that the more fear a woman had surrounding labor and childbirth resulted in a higher likelihood of complications and pain. They named this the fear-tension-pain cycle.

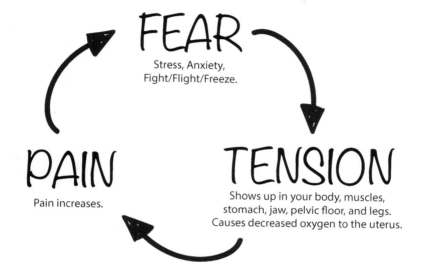

When you feel fearful, anxious, or unsafe, you activate your body's fight, flight, or freeze mode. We see this with Adam and Eve as soon as sin entered the world. I was afraid, so I hid. When you respond to fear, your bloodstream fills with adrenaline, and your body reroutes blood and oxygen away from vital organs (in this case, your uterus) and sends it towards your extremities to help you escape this threat.

Your body thinks it is doing you a favor because it responds to your thoughts or perceived dangers and potential pain. Part of this response causes you to tense up in anticipation of pain. When your muscles are tense, pain increases, and your contractions hurt much more. Agreement with fear, stress, and anxiety perpetuates the cycle.

Fear can also slow your labor down as well as completely stop it for a while. Some women have been laboring when all of a sudden, everything seems to stop progressing altogether. What causes this to happen? A story that illustrates this point is about a deer ready to give birth to her doe. If a deer feels that she is in danger at any time during the labor process or becomes afraid that something is wrong, she can stop her labor in its tracks. She will then move to a place she feels safe and comfortable. Once she feels safe, the labor will pick back up again. The same is true for us. Our minds are influential, and our thoughts tell our bodies what to do. Your body houses the results of the decisions you make.

If you want to break the fear-tension-pain cycle, you must take your thoughts captive and pull down the stronghold of fear. You haven't received a spirit of fear but of perfect love, which casts fear right out.

Science has discovered that Oxytocin, "the love hormone," helps decrease feelings of fear in an individual. Science is the discovery of how God does things! Our body's response to love is a decrease in fear. However, the only way to ultimately cast fear out from your life and your birth experience is through perfect love, which only comes through the Father.

Fear increases pain in birth, but the love of the Father casts fear out. Breathing, methods, knowledge, and affirmations don't cast it out. They may decrease pain symptoms and help you feel less fearful, but only God can eliminate fear.

**God is the source of love and everything good! If you want to experience the fullness of a pain-free birth:**

1. **Yield to Him—Jesus is the only one who has loosed us from pain.**

2. **Immerse and abide in the Father's love.**

### 3. Let perfect love cascade over you through every contraction.

It's good to know how the body works in the natural, but if you want a supernatural birth, you must surrender to the Spirit first and then the body. Surrendering to your contractions and the labor process are very helpful. However, the natural realm has limitations. If you are focusing only on what you are doing naturally, you will get limited results.

**Start first in the spirit.** I always started my labors declaring right away, "I am a daughter of the Most High, and I walk by the spirit and according to His leadings. I willfully submit this labor to You and receive the fullness of all You have for me. My body is responding to Your word, will, and ways. I present my body as a living sacrifice which is my reasonable service. I will not fear, for You are with me. Pain has no power over me because Jesus has loosed it off of my life."

Then speak to your body and surrender your body to the spirit by speaking life. "Mind you will stay in perfect peace the whole time because your thoughts are fixed on Abba, and you trust Him. He is faithful. He is good. Body, you will relax through every contraction. You will birth this baby with ease, confidence, and pain-free. You will dilate quickly and without complications. With you, God, all things are possible."

If you are uneasy, fearful, or anxious about anything, it's a great indicator that you aren't coming from a place of rest but toil. If you find yourself in this state, come to Jesus, who is the giver of rest. Don't wait. You can't get true rest from any other source. *"Come to me, all you who labor and are heavy laden, and I will give you rest."* The word *labor* in this verse means to toil and work hard. Jesus is the one who has broken the curse of toiling, and He is inviting you to partake of what He has to give. *"Take My yoke upon you...For My yoke is easy, and My burden is light." Matthew 11:28–30*

# Fear Is Not Who You Are

To understand the intrusion of fear, we first must know who we are in Christ Jesus. When we know who we are, we won't put up with anything in our lives that doesn't abide in God. Fear is a tool the enemy uses to keep us from the fullness of displaying Christ in us. We are not designed for fear and negativity. God made us in His image, which is love. Love is our true nature.

Fear is not who you are. It is unnatural to our true nature. It is intrusive. Fear and negativity are learned. When you see it as an illegal act of entering, you will close that door real fast. You have the authority to do that because fear is trespassing on private property bought by the blood of Jesus.

The only way fear can stay in your life is if you allow it to. Are you giving fear permission to come and sit with you? Are you giving it a voice in your life? If so, it is time to stand up and say you are no longer welcome here. It is that simple.

If we become fearful through the choices that we have made, we can become fearless by choosing to yield to the Holy Spirit within us. Fear is an enemy that you have victory over. There is no fear in God, and His Spirit lives inside of you. It's time for a fearless generation of women to arise!

There is no reason that we should be walking in fear at any given moment. If you could physically touch and see Jesus in your time of need, when opposition comes your way, or when someone gives you bad news, how would you react?

If a doctor gives you information as your giving birth that strikes fear into your heart, how would you respond differently if Jesus physically walked into your room at that moment? Fear would immediately flee because you know that Jesus can change everything. It wouldn't matter what's been said, for you are staring right at your solution. Jesus, the miracle worker, is standing before you with a big smile on His face waiting for you to welcome Him into your situation.

The truth is that we have Jesus in us at all times, standing with us no matter what we face. He is right there smiling and ready to meet your need. God made known to us the riches of the glory of this mystery, which is Christ in you, the hope of glory.

When troubles come, fix your eyes and thoughts on Jesus and not the problem. When we magnify the problem or the pain, we magnify fear in our lives. Magnifying fear leads to magnified pain. Faith and fear both believe that something that hasn't happened is going to happen. Fear is rooted in bad will happen, but faith is rooted in good will happen. One cancels out the other. On what will you fixate? *As a man thinks in his heart, so is he.* Be intentional about what thoughts you allow to germinate in your head. The thoughts you choose will cause a physical change in your body. If you want to learn more about how your thoughts do this, I highly recommend listening to Dr. Caroline Leaf. She is a spirit-filled cognitive neuroscientist and has many books and teachings on this subject.

When feelings of fear come, don't cave to them. Being afraid is succumbing to fear and doing what fear tells you to do rather than what God tells you to do. Are there areas surrounding conception, pregnancy, birth, postpartum, and motherhood that you are caving to fear or fear of the future? Is it bringing anxiety, stress, and worry? Is it stealing your joy and ripping you off of peace and a sound mind? Every choice you make is a seed you sow that will bring

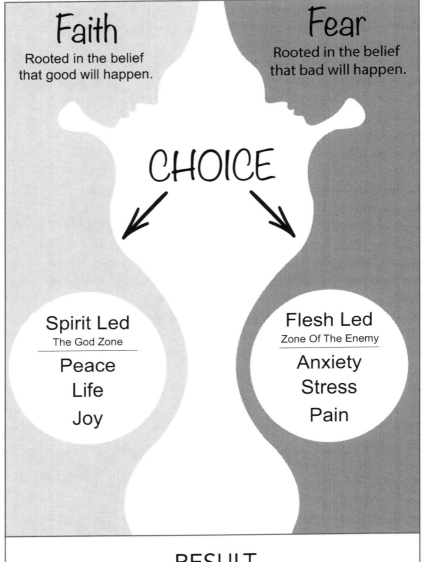

# Faith
Rooted in the belief
that good will happen.

# Fear
Rooted in the belief
that bad will happen.

## CHOICE

### Spirit Led
The God Zone

Peace
Life
Joy

### Flesh Led
Zone Of The Enemy

Anxiety
Stress
Pain

## RESULT

What you choose causes a physical change in your body,
either good or bad. Your body houses the results of the
decisions you make.

about a harvest. If you choose to cave to fear, you will reap torment, for fear involves torment (*1 John 4:18*). It will rip you off of a sound mind.

If Holy Spirit is illuminating anything to you now, break agreement with that fear and choose to fully trust in God, and the peace that surpasses understanding will guard your heart and mind. Staying constant and fearless signifies that we are standing in faith and trust in God while being a sign to the enemy that his day is over!

*And in no way be alarmed or intimidated [in anything] by your opponents, for such [constancy and fearlessness on your part] is a [clear] sign [a proof and a seal] for them of [their impending] destruction, but [a clear sign] for you of deliverance and salvation, and that too, from God. Philippians 1:28 AMP*

# SCRIPTURES ON FEAR

2 Timothy 1:7
For God has not given us a spirit of fear but of power and love and a sound mind.

1 John 4:18
There is no fear in love, but perfect love casts out fear because fear involves torment. But he who fears has not been made perfect in love.

Psalm 34: 4-5
I sought the Lord, and He answered me and delivered me from all my fears. Those who look to Him are radiant, and their faces shall never be ashamed.

John 14:27
Peace I leave with you, My peace I give to you; not as
the world gives do I give to you. Let not your heart be
troubled, neither let it be afraid.

Romans 8:15
For you did not receive the spirit of bondage again to fear,
but you received the Spirit of adoption by whom we cry
out, "Abba, Father."

Isaiah 41:10
Fear not, for I am with you; Be not dismayed, for I am
your God. I will strengthen you; I will help you, I will
uphold you with My righteous right hand.

Psalm 56:3-4
Whenever I am afraid, I will trust in You. In God (I will
praise His word), In God I have put my trust; I will not
fear.

Psalm 27:1
The Lord is my light and my salvation; whom shall I fear?
The Lord is the stronghold of my life; of whom shall I be
afraid?

Genesis 50:21
Do not be afraid; I will provide for you and your little
ones.

Isaiah 43:1
But now, thus says the Lord, who created you, O Jacob,
And He who formed you, O Israel: "Fear not, for I have
redeemed you; I have called you by your name; You are
Mine.

Joshua 1:9

Have I not commanded you? Be strong and of good
courage; do not be afraid, nor be dismayed, for the Lord
your God is with you wherever you go.

Isaiah 41:13

For I, the Lord your God will hold your right hand,
Saying to you, 'Fear not, I will help you.'

Mark 5:36

Do not be afraid; only believe.

Lamentations 3:57

You came near when I called on You and said, "Do not
fear!'

Luke 12:32

Fear not, for it is your Father's good pleasure to give you
the Kingdom.

Psalm 91:1-16

He who dwells in the secret place of the Most High
Shall abide under the shadow of the Almighty. I will say of
the Lord, "He is my refuge and my fortress;
My God, in Him I will trust."
Surely He shall deliver you from the snare of the fowler,
And from the perilous pestilence.
He shall cover you with His feathers,
And under His wings you shall take refuge;
His truth shall be your shield and buckler.
You shall not be afraid of the terror by night,
Nor of the arrow that flies by day,
Nor of the pestilence that walks in darkness,
Nor of the destruction that lays waste at noonday.

A thousand may fall at your side,
And ten thousand at your right hand;
But it shall not come near you.
Only with your eyes shall you look,
And see the reward of the wicked.
Because you have made the Lord, who is my refuge,
Even the Most High, your dwelling place,
No evil shall befall you,
Nor shall any plague come near your dwelling;
For He shall give His angels charge over you,
To keep you in all your ways.
In their hands, they shall bear you up,
Lest you dash your foot against a stone.
You shall tread upon the lion and the cobra,
The young lion and the serpent you shall trample underfoot.
"Because he has set his love upon Me, therefore I will deliver him;
I will set him on high because he has known My name.
He shall call upon Me, and I will answer him;
I will be with him in trouble;
I will deliver him and honor him.
With long life I will satisfy him,
And show him My salvation."

# TRAUMA

Many women have experienced trauma in their life. Many different things can cause trauma, such as an accident, sickness, abuse, sexual abuse, and abortions. The most common emotional reaction to trauma is shame, fear, and anxiety.

Our minds may tend to replay the memory, or something can

trigger a flashback. These are upsetting because they tend to bring back a mighty flood of emotions and vivid memories of the event. I once was stuck in this emotional cycle of pain. My mind became easily triggered, which would throw me into a tailspin of emotions. Then I would try to disconnect from my soul, which is the mind, will, and emotions. That only left me numb and powerless. I never knew I could walk in complete freedom from even the memories of sexual abuse.

*1 John 3:2*
*Beloved, I pray that you may prosper in all things and be in health, just as your soul prospers.*

My soul needed healing. I wanted to prosper in all things, including my soul, but I didn't know-how. Honestly, I didn't even realize this was something available to me. I never correlated the fact that Jesus suffered a traumatic death to overcome trauma for humankind. Trauma could not keep him in the grave.

Jesus is sitting at the Father's right hand in a place of rest, the finished work. This truth renewed my mind to realize that trauma no longer had power over me either. I am seated and at rest, for I have been raised with Him and have been made to sit together in heavenly places.

Jesus broke the stronghold of trauma on the cross. The battle has been won. Jesus didn't die for me to keep struggling and fighting my way through life. He died, rose again, and left His Spirit to empower me to walk in total victory. When I renewed my mind to this truth, I began to walk in freedom from all trauma symptoms.

What does trauma have to do with childbirth? I thought the same thing as I sat in my midwife's office for the first time filling out paperwork for my first pregnancy. The paperwork contained a section that specifically asked very personal questions. These questions included, have you experienced sexual abuse, or have you been raped?

I remember reading that, and my heart starting to pound faster. I wasn't expecting this trigger at my first pregnancy appointment. I thought that was an odd question. Why would they need this kind of information? I sat there for a few minutes, trying to decide if I even wanted to answer that question. Then I heard the still small voice of God say, "ask the midwife why they ask this question in the paperwork." My mind is now going all over the place.

God asks me to confront the issue, and I want to ignore it and stuff it like I always have. Now I'm sitting there waiting to be called on and dreading every moment. I had a choice to make. Will I do as God says, or will I let my emotions dominate me. The struggle was real. I was used to being dominated by my emotions. Little did I know that this simple Rhema Word of God would change everything.

I decided to do what God said. As I sat in the beautiful birthing room talking to the midwife, I paused and asked her the dreaded question. "Why did you ask me in the paperwork if I was raped or sexually abused? What does that have to do with childbirth?" She replied and said she knew it seemed like an odd question, but that sexual trauma can affect labor because both sexual abuse and childbirth involve the same body areas. Sexual trauma can affect a woman's ability to trust the birthing process and may be triggered during the birth. She said it was common enough that they wanted to be equipped to help women and be prepared.

I was shocked as I listened to her. I experienced both sexual abuse and rape. I knew it was time to deal with some stuff. I had no idea that this trauma had the potential to affect so many parts of my life. Now I'm being told it could directly affect my children. That was sobering to me. It jolted me out of my cycle of numbing to cope and made me determined to break it.

I went to counseling in the past, so I hadn't been entirely ignoring the problem all this time. However, I was not free from this trauma, and I knew it. Something shifted in me as I left that appointment. It was the beginning of partnering with God to walk in power and no longer as a victim.

The trauma created a victim mindset. I saw my entire life through a perspective that bad things would happen to me. I also expected people to mistreat me. It didn't matter if I said no or didn't like how I was being treated because I figured my no wasn't important to people. I believed they would take advantage of me anyway. I felt like my voice didn't matter. I partnered with these feelings, which is what the enemy wanted all along. He tried to silence me forever. This mindset kept me in a constant state of allowing people to walk all over me. I believed I was powerless. This perspective was not grounded in the truth.

If you don't think your voice matters, you won't assert yourself during the birth process. If you find yourself stuck in a victim mindset, know that you are not meant to live there. You must break your alliance with bad belief systems and lies trying to distort your perspective and keep you powerless. Partner with God and begin to lay a new foundation of truth.

A practical example from my story is that I chose no longer to agree that bad things would happen to me and that I was powerless. I then intentionally planted and partnered with the truth. I searched scriptures that spoke the truth into this situation and meditated on them day and night. Here are a few scripture examples that replaced my belief in a bad future and powerlessness.

# The truth is, it's always going to end well!

*Romans 8:28*
*And we know that all things work together for good to those who love God, to those who are the called according to His purpose.*

*Psalm 23:6*
*Surely goodness and mercy shall follow me ALL the days of my life.*

# The truth is I have power!

*Ephesians 3:14,16*
*For this reason, I bow my knees to the Father of our Lord Jesus Christ... that He would grant you, according to the riches of His glory, to be strengthened with power through His Spirit in the inner man.*

*2 Timothy 1:7*
*For God has not given us a spirit of fear, but of power and of love and of a sound mind.*

The road to renewing the mind may not always be easy, but God is good and faithful to help us step into victory. I am no longer a victim, and I don't carry a victim mindset. Praise God!

Renewing my mind with truth directly affected each one of my births. I believed I was powerful, which led to being in complete control of my labor instead of feeling like a victim and powerless. I expected a good outcome instead of believing that something bad would happen.

Not only did I expect good, I exclusively partnered with "good" no matter what arose. I was filled with joy and birthed my babies with total confidence. That in and of itself is a miracle! Whom the Son sets free is free indeed.

## Prayer

Father, I need your healing touch over the trauma that has taken place in my life. I forgive_____ for the trauma they caused in my life. I take authority over the stronghold of any trauma in my soul and body, and I tear it down in Jesus' name. I renounce and cast out the spirits of abandonment, fear, perversion, abuse of all kinds, and insecurity in Jesus' name. I allow the overflow of healing into my entire being. Thank you, Jesus, that you have made me whole. I receive my healing right now. Thank you, Father, for delivering me from the spirit of trauma.

In Jesus' name AMEN

## Abortion

If you have had an abortion, that does not mean you are disqualified from having a pain-free supernatural birth. I saw a vision that the enemy is harassing women in the body of Christ because of a past abortion. He was whispering words of condemnation. These lies were keeping women from walking in the full blessing that is their rightful inheritance. Their heads hung down, full of shame and guilt.

The precious blood of Jesus bought our inheritance. Our faith, good works, performance, or anything that we do does not buy the blessing. We receive it by faith. It is a gift (grace). It is time to get rid of sin consciousness, and we need to dwell in the mindset of who we are in Christ Jesus.

*2 Corinthians 5:17*
*Therefore, if anyone is in Christ, he is a new creation; old things*
*have passed away; behold, all things have become new.*

Any lie of the enemy that says you are not worthy, you are not holy, or that the things you have done in the past will keep you from being blessed today is a flat-out lie.

*Romans 8:1*
*There is therefore now no condemnation to those who are*
*in Christ Jesus, who do not walk according to the flesh, but*
*according to the Spirit.*

You are no longer in bondage to the things of the flesh. You have been awakened and reborn according to the Spirit. You have been crucified with Christ. It is no longer I who live, but Christ lives in me; the life I now live in the flesh I live by faith in God's Son. By faith, you live in the Son of God completely new, born again.

All condemning voices and thoughts that try to pull you out of the truth that you are righteous, perfect, and holy must go. I hear these verses being declared over you today.

*Isaiah 61:7*
*Instead of your shame, you will receive a double portion, and*
*instead of disgrace, you will rejoice in your inheritance. And so*
*you will inherit a double portion in your land, and everlasting*
*joy will be yours.*

*Isaiah 54:17*
*"No weapon formed against you shall prosper, And every tongue*
*which rises against you in judgment you shall condemn. This is*
*the heritage of the servants of the Lord, and their righteousness is*
*from Me," says the Lord.*

# Prayer

Father, I come boldly to your throne of grace, and I rejoice in the truth that if I confess my sins, you are faithful and just to forgive me of all unrighteousness and cleanse me from all sin; this includes abortion. I confess my abortion to you, and I declare that I will be completely free from all shame and guilt of the abortion from this day forward. I will walk by faith and not by what I feel, believing everything You say about me.

I rebuke and will no longer partner with any accusations about my past that the enemy brings up to hinder me from walking in victory and the fullness of my inheritance in Christ Jesus. I realize that I gave the enemy legal right to my body through abortion, but I thank you that as I have confessed this sin unto you, every door has been shut to the enemy to torment me in my mind and body. I am free, for who the Son sets free is free indeed! Thank you, Jesus, for freedom.

In Jesus' name AMEN

(Read Declarations On The Next Page)

# Declarations

I am the righteousness of Christ.

I am holy and blameless before you.

I am accepted.

I am loved.

I am seated with Christ in heavenly places.

I have all things under my feet.

I am rooted and grounded in Christ's love.

My soul prospers.

Instead of shame, I receive a double portion.

Instead of disgrace, I rejoice in my inheritance.

Joy is mine.

A double portion is my inheritance here on earth.

# I Birth Pain-Free

# CHAPTER 8

You have believed in a pain-free supernatural birth throughout your pregnancy, you've meditated on God's Word, and you have faithfully made declarations. Now labor kicks in, and it is finally go-time. I've had women say that I believed and did my part, but I started to have pain, and what I believed for didn't work. Just because pain shows up does not make God's Word null and void. Yield to God's Word, which doesn't return void and not the pain. It takes effort on our part. That is where the rubber meets the road, and you will need to boot unbelief out, stand in faith and persevere.

Resist the devil, and he will flee. Pain, fear, sickness, doubt, unbelief, anxiety, worry, complications in your pregnancy or labor are not from God. These come from the devil. The Word of God does not say to submit to those things. It says to submit to God, not your emotions, thoughts, pain, or even what others say about the situation. After you submit to God, then resist the devil, and he will flee. It doesn't say he might flee; it says he *WILL* flee.

Anytime these things try to come upon you, you must take action. Resist it. If a thief grabbed my purse, I wouldn't say, "take it; it's all yours." No way! I would resist him and take hold of what belongs to me. The devil is a thief, and you must resist him and take hold of what belongs to you.

Jesus showed us how to resist the devil when he was tempted in the wilderness. "It is written." The sword of the Spirit is a powerful weapon. It is the Word of God. The devil can not overpower it, for it is truth. He knows it but doesn't want you to know it. He twists the truth in hopes that you agree with his words and question the Word of God instead of the other way around. It's the same tactic he used in the beginning when he asked Eve, "Did God really say?"

Now in the wilderness, we see satan posing a new question aimed at Jesus, "if you are the son of God." It was a direct attack on the spoken Word of God given to Jesus right before the wilderness account. Jesus heard from the Father while being water baptized by John the Baptist, "You are my beloved son in whom I am well pleased." Satan tells Jesus if you are the son of God, prove it.

It is essential you know the schemes of the devil. There are two schemes we see the devil use through the fall of man and when Jesus was tempted.

-> The enemy wants you to question what God has said.

-> The enemy wants you to question who you are.

He wants you to prove yourself instead of resting in the knowledge that you are already approved.

The enemy targets the Word of God you have received because you believing what God says is a threat to the powers of darkness to steal, kill, and destroy. If we don't understand this, we think that we are doing something wrong when opposition comes every time

God speaks a word into our life. The devil has power, but he has no authority.

Jesus said in *Mathew 28:18, "All authority in heaven and on earth has been given to me."* Jesus has all authority, and he gives us authority over all the power of the enemy. He said to them, *"I saw Satan fall like lightning from heaven. Behold, I give you the authority to trample on serpents and scorpions, and over all the power of the enemy, and nothing shall by any means hurt you. Nevertheless, do not rejoice in this, that the spirits are subject to you, but rather rejoice because your names are written in heaven." Luke 10:18-20.*

You have authority over all the power of the enemy. He is powerless every time you step into the room. The authority you carry freaks him out and causes him to flee. The only way he stands a chance is if you doubt and question the very words of God and choose to submit to the lie. He is empowered only through agreement.

You need to shut him up by submitting to the truth and speaking the Word of God. Every demonic spirit is subject to us and not the other way around. We are victorious! Stand firm in this truth. The devil will flee because he will see that this woman doesn't mess around. It is time to rise women of God and be a force to be reckoned with. Use your authority in Christ, Jesus!!

All that is done leading up to labor prepares you for the big moment and gives you the tools to succeed even if opposition comes. For instance, I played sports my whole life. Basketball was my favorite. All the practices I attended and the hard work I put in was all to prepare me for game time. It would be silly to do all that and then quit after the first quarter of the game because we perceive we aren't winning. That attitude says, "well, it seems all my hard work isn't paying off. I should throw in the towel." Even in the natural world, everyone would say, "Hey, the game is not over yet.

You are just getting started. You've got this. Believe in yourself, get out there, and persevere until the end. It's not over until it's over." How much more ridiculous is it to throw in the towel when you are guaranteed victory.

You see, all the work leading up to the moment prepares you for what to do when opposition comes. When it gets tough, don't leave the game. The enemy wins by default if you do that. Put your faith into action, for faith without works is dead. Faith that doesn't involve action is phony. *Hebrews 11:1 says, "Now faith is the substance of things hoped for and the evidence of things not seen."*

If you put your faith in what you see and how you feel, you are putting your faith in the natural realm. Spiritual faith is different. You believe it first, then you receive it. You believe that you have received a pain-free supernatural birth before you have received it. Smith Wigglesworth states it well when he said, "I'm not moved by what I see. I'm not moved by what I feel. I'm only moved by what I believe."

When labor starts, what do you do if symptoms of pain come? Let's get practical. I've heard women say; I won't say I'm not having pain when I am. That statement shows me where your faith lies. That kind of faith is in the natural realm because it is dependant on what you see and feel. Remember, spiritual faith believes in the unseen. If discomfort, pain, or complications come, speak the truth of God's Word over the situation instead of speaking what is happening in the natural. God's Word supersedes the natural realm, changes the atmosphere, and flips the script.

For example, if I set my house thermostat to 60 degrees and it's too cold for me, I don't just look at it and say, oh well, I guess I'm stuck being cold. I wouldn't do that because I can change the temperature to what I want to have. I take action and reset the temperature. When I reset the temperature to 70 degrees, I don't hope it will change; I know it will change. I expect it!

You will have the same result when you speak God's Word over any symptoms of pain. Don't stay stuck in pain. Set your thermostat by your thoughts and back your thoughts up with your words. If your words don't match with the truth of God's Word, then you know you need to take some thoughts captive and renew your mind. Think of your thought life as your thermostat.

When the symptoms come, what do you believe? By our words, our faith is speaking. You can't live by faith without talking faith. Faith is released through words. You can be defeated by your words as in Proverbs 6:2, which says, *"You are snared by the words of your mouth. You are taken by the words of your mouth."* Or you can be victorious by your words, as in Mark 11:23-24. *"Have faith in God. For assuredly, I say to you; whoever says to this mountain, 'Be removed and be cast into the sea,' and does not doubt in his heart, but believes that those things he says will be done, he will have whatever he says. Therefore I say to you, whatever things you ask when you pray, believe that you receive them, and you will have them."*

There are two kingdom keys here that I want to point out in these verses. If you get this revelation, it will shift everything in your life. The first key is that the speaking precedes the possessing and not the other way around. Jesus doesn't say when the mountain is removed speak. You wouldn't need to speak up if nothing was in your way. He says to speak to the mountain (the pain), and you will have whatever you say. He doesn't say to speak to the mountain, and you might get what you say. He says you WILL have what you say. You will have 100% results if you do this believing and not doubting. We know Jesus can't lie to us, so this must be true.

The first key involves commanding. You aren't commanding God to do anything because He has already done it; you are commanding the pain to go. Everything that is not from God is in opposition to Him, and He has given us authority to remove any opposition that gets in the way of the Kingdom being released. In this case, it would be pain, fear, complications, sickness, or whatever might come against you during pregnancy and labor.

The second key involves prayer and asking. After Jesus explains the first key, He then ties it to prayer so that when we pray, we will be effective. He wants us to get this revelation.

The key here is that you must believe that you receive whatever you ask for when you pray. Prayer is believing and receiving. When do you receive what you asked for in prayer? The moment you prayed. Not when you have it. Mind-blowing, isn't it.

When you prayed and asked God for an easy, quick, supernatural, and pain-free labor, what do you believe about what you just asked for in prayer? Your faith is always speaking. What are the words coming out of your mouth? For out of the abundance of the heart, the mouth speaks.

Are you saying things like, we will see what happens? I hope God answers this prayer for me. Those statements reveal that you did not ask, believing that you have received. Therefore you won't have what you have requested.

*But let him ask in faith, with no doubting, for he who doubts is like a wave of the sea driven and tossed by the wind. For let not that man suppose that he will receive anything from the Lord; he is a double-minded man, unstable in all his ways.*
*James 1:6-8*

Doubting looks like not believing that you have received what you ask for, and that kind of person is double-minded, unstable in all their ways. In other words, your speech should sound like you already have what you asked. Doubt can also look like begging and worrying about it. Faith, on the other hand, knows it is settled. When you know it's settled, you can shout it out for all to hear and rejoice in total confidence.

# Fight or Surrender

I want to clarify that when you go into labor, you mustn't go into fight mode. Remember that fight mode is activated when you feel fearful, anxious, or unsafe, leading to the fear, tension, and pain cycle. All that I stated before is to help you prepare for birth by learning your inheritance and authority in Christ, so you don't let go of the promise.

The state you should be in for labor should look like what Jesus did when opposition arose as He traveled in the boat to get to the other side? He slept! A great storm arose, and the disciples were in pure panic mode as the boat started filling up with water. They were scared, but Jesus stayed in a place of total peace and rest. He was unphased by the opposition. From this state of fearlessness and rest, He arose and spoke peace to the storm. It obeyed Him.

Jesus was so aware of who He was and His purpose it was easy to walk fearlessly in power. He spoke from a place of authority because He possessed it in His being first. Out of the abundance of the heart, the mouth speaks. He rebuked the storm with one phrase, "Peace, be still!"

Everything we do should come from a place of rest. It's easy to rest when you are fully yielded and surrendered to the King of Kings, who has overcome it all. Be so intentional in renewing your mind that it doesn't matter what is happening around you. No matter what, you should always feel safe and secure and able to assert your authority from a place of fearlessness. Renew your mind until your unshakable.

Your mind and body need to stay in a perfect state of peace while laboring. How do we do this? Surrender! Surrender equals trust.

*Isaiah 26:3*
*You will keep him in perfect peace, whose mind is stayed on You because he trusts in You.*

Pain-free childbirth comes from great surrender. Trust God and trust that He designed your body perfectly for birth. Just like Jesus and the disciples, you will get to the other side. Will you get there panicking or in a state of total peace? Jesus' internal state of peace affected the physical realm with one phrase. If you strive for anything, strive to ENTER REST!

# Sphincter Law

Our bodies respond to how we feel and perceive things. Have you ever heard of the sphincter law? A sphincter is a ring of muscle surrounding and serving to guard or close an opening. Your cervix is a sphincter that opens to pass your baby from your uterus. Contractions are the muscles opening your cervix, and dilation is the measurement of the opening of your cervix.

If you are tense, uncomfortable, feeling exposed, or pressured to push before you are ready, the softening of your cervix can stall, slowing labor down. Trying to force a baby through the cervix before it is ready puts undue pressure on your pelvic floor, and that can lead to tearing.

Pushing happens spontaneously without guidance from someone else. The muscles open more efficiently in a comfortable atmosphere where you feel safe. When a mother feels safe and cared for, her body will respond by opening up, and the baby will come quickly with less stress. On the other hand, sphincter muscles may suddenly close if the woman feels threatened in any way, is scared, doesn't feel safe, or is startled by rough handling.

Sphincters function best in an atmosphere of privacy and familiarity. For example, it is easier to poop in a toilet that you are familiar with than a public toilet. Similarly, it is easier to give birth in your home than in a sterile hospital room. If you are birthing in a hospital, be intentional about adding some familiar touches to the room to make you feel more comfortable.

If you keep getting interrupted while you are laboring with people coming in and out of the room, your sphincter may close as well. Think about when you are on the toilet mid-pee, and someone walks in on you. What happens? The pee stops flowing. The same thing happens with your cervical sphincter. Protecting a mom's comfort and safety is essential in achieving a natural birth that progresses easily and quickly.

If you are feeling tense or scared, try laughing. Laughter relaxes sphincter muscles. A merry heart does a spirit, soul, and body good like a medicine. Laughter and joy can turn things around.

**I Am Anointed With Joy Throughout The Birth Experience.**

*God has anointed you with the oil of gladness.*

*Psalm 45:7*

# Contractions Are Good!

As you can see, it is essential to feel safe and secure when laboring. Everything flows better, and your body responds by creating more muscular contractions opening you up. Strong contractions are good! That means your body is doing its job. You need to welcome your contractions because they are there to help you birth your baby.

Your uterus can contract without pain because I have done it four times. It is entirely possible. If you happen to feel any pain symptoms while laboring, I want to give you a very practical tool that will help.

First, know a contraction and pain are two different things. They are not one, so welcome every contraction with joy because it brings you closer to meeting your baby. Then visualize Jesus taking pain upon himself and carrying it away from you. He has overcome pain, and so can you.

# Welcome Every Contraction

- Visualize each contraction, opening you up more and more.

- Thank your contraction for doing its job well.

- Fully embrace and surrender to what your body needs to do to birth with ease.

# Jesus Took The Pain

+ Visualize Jesus carrying pain away from your body.

+ Thank Jesus for nailing pain to the cross.

+ Fully embrace and surrender to resurrection life flowing through you.

# Fearless Faith

# CHAPTER 9

It is easy to believe in a pain-free supernatural birth when believers surround you, and everyone is flowing together in faith. However, when you are in the world and surrounded by unbelievers, it becomes more difficult. There is opposition. Remaining in fearless faith that doesn't waver is tough when the world's way of thinking is bombarding you. It takes a lot of courage and boldness to go against the constant negative current. Be ready to stand out and be different.

I want to share the story of manna with you because it foreshadows so much about Jesus, faith, and our walk with Christ. Did you realize that manna was like coriander seed and was the color of bdellium? According to Numbers 11:7-9, the people went out and gathered this seed and had to grind it on millstones or beat it in the mortar. After this, they were able to cook it in pans and make cakes out of it.

First, notice that God provided the seed, but the people were responsible for making it into food. Most Christians believe that the Israelites had entirely made bread fall on the ground and that the people didn't need to do anything, but that is not what the Bible says. God wants us to partner with Him.

He has provided everything we need, but we won't enjoy the blessing if we don't do our part. In fact, hearing the Word of the Lord is what made the Israelites know that they could even make the manna that fell from heaven into bread. He told them before they had the manifestation that He would send bread from heaven. Faith comes by hearing and hearing the Word of God. When the Israelites saw their answer manifested, they looked at it and said, "what is it?" They had no idea what it was. Manna means what is it? Moses answered them by saying it was the bread that the Lord has given you to eat.

What the Israelites were receiving from heaven had to be spiritually discerned to know what to do with it. That discernment came from hearing the Word of God. The Israelites were responsible for responding to the Word. They had to act on it to benefit from the blessing freely given to them. Did they have to put some time and energy into it? Yes! Did it take some physical work? Yes! Did they receive the blessing because of their works? No. It was a gift. Could they enjoy the gift without their works? No.

"What does it profit if someone says he has faith but does not have works? Faith by itself, if it does not have works, is dead. But someone will say, 'You have faith, and I have works.' Show me your faith without your works, and I will show you my faith by my works. Was not Abraham our father justified by works when he offered Isaac his son on the altar? Do you see that faith was working together with his works, and by works faith was made perfect? And the scripture was fulfilled, which says, 'Abraham believed God, and it was accounted to him for righteousness.' And he was called the friend of God. You see then that man was justified by works, and not by faith only." (*James 2*)

Within the story of manna, notice that the Israelites were to take a certain amount of manna per person. Everyone was to get the same amount, which was an omer. An omer is an ancient Israelite unit of dry measure for grains and dry commodities. It is equal to one-tenth of an ephah. Each person was to go out and gather only an omer of the grain of manna per day. Likewise, everyone has been given the measure of faith.

*Romans 12:3*
*For I say, through the grace given to me, to everyone who is among you, not to think of himself more highly than he ought to think but to think soberly, as God has dealt to each one the measure of faith.*

*Ephesians 2:8-9*
*For by grace you have been saved through faith, and that not of yourselves; it is the gift of God, not of works, lest anyone should boast.*

We have all been given the measure of faith. If works could obtain your faith, then you could boast, but that is not the case. It is a gift, a spiritual blessing, not of ourselves. Faith doesn't buy the blessing. Jesus purchased the blessing with his blood, and I receive it by faith. By faith, I believe that Jesus is the Son of God, died, rose again, and is seated at the Father's right hand. Jesus is the bread that came down from heaven (*John 6:51*). To enjoy all the benefits, I need to respond to Him, act on His Word, and walk it out daily. Faith stirs the heart to glorify God through practical actions.

Faith is also an act of surrender. Are you surrendering to the faith of God or the faith of the world? The God kind of faith is the evidence of things not seen. The faith of God has its origin in Him. That is why spiritual faith comes by hearing His Word.

Faith is how you reach out and take something from the unseen realm and bring it into the physical realm. Faith pleases God, for it brings heaven to earth. We need faith because it is the key to unlocking the spiritual realm into our lives. The enemy knows this also, so satan lies to us about it. He wants us to believe that we don't have faith or enough faith. He wants us to compare ourselves to others and think that they have more faith than we do. He wants us to agree with that lie to keep us from being effective.

The truth is that we have all received the same measure of faith. I do not have more faith than you and vice versa. Grace, salvation, and faith is the gift of God. It doesn't come from us and our workings. We can not boast that we are the source of any of these things.

Next time the devil starts lying to you about your level of faith, you stand up tall and smack him in the face with the Word of God, if you catch my drift. Declare I have been given the measure of faith. My God's divine power has given me all things pertaining to life and godliness, and everything I will ever need has already been given to me and is in me through Jesus. Amen

Satan wants you to think that faith is the problem, but it is not. Jesus made it a point to let us know that we don't need giant faith to move mountains. It only takes mustard seed faith. If you are born again, you have mustard seed faith.

The problem isn't our faith or "the size of our faith," but rather in realizing what we have and acting on it. If we don't know what we have, we won't use it, and then we miss our blessing. Like the Israelites, we are walking around saying, "what is it?" We need the revelation of what exactly came down from heaven (Jesus), all that has been provided to us through Him, and we need to know how to use it in our life. Faith works when we realize what we have. *"I pray that your faith may become effective by the acknowledgment of every good thing which is in you in Christ Jesus." Philemon 1:6*

We want our faith to be effective. To be effective, we must acknowledge every good thing in us in Jesus! Take the time to find out every good thing that is in you. Study it, meditate on it, believe it, and declare it!

Ephesians, chapters one, two, and three are a good starting point to recognize what we have in Jesus. One of the things we should know is that God has blessed us with every spiritual blessing in the heavenly places in Christ (Ephesians 1:3). Spiritual blessings are more real than the physical realm. The physical realm is dying and decaying. Everything you touch and see is not exactly what it will be in the future.

For instance, if you buy a new car, in 10 years it will look different because it decays. There is less hope in the physical realm. Even though you may not see the spiritual realm with your eyes, it is more real and more substantial than the physical realm because it doesn't decay. It is eternal.

What blessings are in heavenly places? Think about it. Is there fear, lack, worry, sickness, disease, strife, pain, lies, chaos, division, and so forth in heaven? No. The word spiritual here is pneumatikos, which means the realm of the Spirit that has its origin in God. Every spiritual blessing has its origin in God.

On the other hand, things like fear, doubt, and sickness do not originate from God. Suppose I'm a woman that trusts in my abilities, and I believe in fearless, pain-free childbirth and do everything about pregnancy and childbirth with my abilities. In that case, my labor and childbirth origin is in the physical realm, the flesh. However, if my whole pregnancy and childbirth experience is rooted in trusting God and His abilities, now the blessing is different. This labor and pregnancy have their origin in God. It's supernatural!

God is Spirit, and He made everything in the physical realm. Hebrews 11:3 says, *"By faith we understand that the worlds were framed by the word of God, so that the things which are seen were not made of things which are visible."* This scripture says that the spiritual realm brings forth the physical realm and not the other way around. All your answers are in the Spirit, and it is the Spirit that manifests in the physical realm. It's the way it works. What you want to see in the physical will be added to you if you seek first the Kingdom and His righteousness.

The worlds were framed by the *rhema* (word) of God. Rhema means a spoken word made "by the living voice." The earth, which contains everything we see now, was not made from the visible realm. It came into existence by the *rhema* word of God. He spoke it, and it became a reality. We understand this by faith, and by faith the elders obtained a good testimony. In essence, you can read it like this, the elders heard God talk to them, and by faith they grabbed hold of His spoken Word and saw it come to pass in their life because everything God says has the power to become a reality.

God penetrates the invisible realm with His spoken words. "Now faith comes by hearing and hearing the word of God." The word used here is *rhema*. So faith comes by hearing and hearing the spoken word of God. It is your job to incline your ear to listen to what God is saying to you. Faith comes by hearing God speak to you!

When you read your Bible, don't just read the passage and check off the religious box of duty. Instead, say, God, what are you speaking to me today? Listen for His voice as you read the scriptures, as you pray, as you cook, as you engage with your children, and as you hang out with your husband.

We do not live by bread alone, but by every word that proceeds out of the mouth of God. Rhema is used again here in this scripture for word. We are to live by what God is saying. We thrive with a personal relationship with the Father. We are to live in constant conversation and communion with Him. We should read all scripture and listen to what God is saying to us personally!

Scripture is not dead. It is alive and active. Until you hear God saying it to you, it doesn't bring faith. If you read scripture as just a passage, it's just a promise in the Bible. When you read scripture and hear God speaking it over your life, it becomes YOUR promise. Then it becomes alive to us and in us. Hearing God speak to us personally is when faith gets activated.

# DOUBT AND UNBELIEF

We know we need faith, and we are confident we have it. However, if the size of our faith isn't the problem, what is? It comes down to doubt and unbelief. You can have both faith and doubt at the same time. If you operate in doubt at any given time, God does not take back the gift of faith. You still have faith; you just have chosen not to act in it at that moment. It happens. It isn't always easy to believe, especially in the waiting.

To work the works of God, we must believe. When multitudes followed Jesus because of the signs and miracles, they asked Him what they needed to do to operate in the works of God. Jesus replied that the work of God is to believe (adhere to, trust in, rely on, and have faith) in Him (*John 6: 28-29*).

Unbelief is the reason that the disciples could not cast out the demon and heal the epileptic boy. The disciples had the authority to do it and had already worked many signs and wonders. They had faith, but their unbelief suppressed it at this moment. Jesus was not very pleased with their inability to do what He called them to do. He said, *"O faithless and perverse generation, how long must I be with you? How long shall I bear with you? Bring him here to Me." Matthew 17:17*. Perverse means to do something contrary to the accepted or expected standard or practice. It means to turn away from what is right or good; to be wrongheaded.

The disciples chose at that moment to turn from faith, the right way of thinking, and step into unbelief, which is wrongheaded. We know that unbelief was the problem because scripture says that they asked Jesus privately why they couldn't cast out the demon. Jesus said it was because of their unbelief. He did not say it was their lack of faith.

He reminded them that they only needed mustard seed faith to move mountains. Unbelief was the hindrance, and Jesus said that this kind of unbelief does not go except by prayer and fasting *(Matthew 17:20-21)*. Fasting gets rid of unbelief because it makes you put your body in subjection to the things of the Spirit. Your body and your senses no longer dominate, but your Spirit.

The disciples could not work the works of God to cure the boy with unbelief in their hearts. At this point, the boy's father has his doubts too. Once the disciples failed to cure the boy, he asked Jesus to help him if He could. Jesus said if I can? All things are possible to him who believes. The father yells out, then I believe, please help my unbelief. Although the truth of Jesus' words provokes us to deal with our heart's motives, he does not mind our honesty. He is moved by us boldly coming for help.

Jesus is the High Priest over your confession, and what a great High Priest He is. *"Seeing then that we have a great High Priest, who has passed through the heavens, Jesus, the Son of God, let us hold fast our confession" Hebrews 4:14*. He understands us and sympathizes with our weaknesses because He was tempted in all areas as we are just without sin. He understands the doubt that we so easily succumb to and why we waver. So come boldly to the throne of grace and find grace to help in time of need. He is ready, willing, and able to move on your confession, so hold fast to it. He is anointed and appointed by God to bring it to pass.

In the waiting is when it's easy to give in to doubt. We must hold fast to the confession of our faith and persevere. *"Let us hold fast the confession of our faith without wavering; for He is faithful that promised." Hebrews 10:23.* God is good, and He is faithful. If I was stranded on the side of the road and called my husband to come and get me, I know that he would follow through on his word. If someone else pulled over and said they would give me a ride home, I would say that's ok my husband is on his way. My confession matches what I believe about my husband. It's easy for me to confess that to a total stranger because I know my husband's character. Likewise, God's character is proven. He is faithful who promised.

In *Psalm 116:10,* David says, I believed; therefore, I have spoken. The apostles quote this in *2 Corinthians 4:13,* saying that they carry the same Spirit of faith because we believe; therefore, we speak. Through faith, we believe, confess, and testify. We must remain steadfast in agreeing with God and what He says no matter what we think, feel, or see in the natural. It takes effort, intentionality, persistence, and patience. Keep a firm grip on the promises, for God always keeps His word.

# Walk By Faith Not Sight

It is inevitable for our faith to get tested. However, we are to count it all joy no matter the trials we face in this lifetime because we know that when faith gets tested, it stirs up power within us to endure all things. It produces patience, and patient endurance releases perfection into every part of your being until nothing is missing and nothing is lacking. We are to imitate those who inherit the promises through faith and patience (*Hebrews 6:12*).

Step out in fearless faith! Faith has nothing to do with what we see because faith is the substance of things hoped for, and hope that is seen is not hope. Why does one still hope for what he sees? *"But if we hope for what we do not see, we eagerly wait for it with perseverance." (Romans 8:24).* Unwavering faith produces patience. You can not have faith without hope. If you are losing hope, you are letting go of the substance of faith, which leads to grabbing hold of the substance of doubt.

In Greek, the word substance also means foundation. If you lose hope, you are setting your foundation in doubt. Teeter-tottering between faith and doubt makes you unstable, wavering back and forth. You are half-hearted, not fully committed. Decide to be wholehearted. *"Now may the God of hope fill you with all joy and peace in believing, that you may abound in hope by the power of the Holy Spirit."Romans 15:13.*

Walk by faith and not by sight. Natural sight limits us, but faith sees things greater than what the natural eyes can see. Sometimes it is hard to let go and believe. It is easier to cling to what we see. Although, if we want to step into the supernatural, we can not cling to the natural realm. God's truth supersedes any circumstance.

Knowing that we are in a spiritual battle, God gave His only begotten Son. Together they conquered sin, death, and the curse. The war has been won, and now we are more than conquerors. Take courage; He has overcome the world, and so do we. Every child of God overcomes the world, for our faith is the victorious power that triumphs over the world. So who are the world conquerors defeating its power? Those who believe that Jesus is the Son of God (*1 John 5:4–5*).

# Renewing The Mind

RENEWING THE MIND    141

# CHAPTER 10

The true you is your Spirit. You have a soul (which is your mind, will, and emotions) that lives in a body. Your brain is the physical part of you that controls your entire body. In essence, your Spirit controls your soul, and your soul controls your body. God ultimately designed your Spirit to be led by the Holy Spirit.

The proper order looks like this.

$$\text{Holy Spirit} \Rrightarrow \text{Soul} \Rrightarrow \text{Body}$$

Your body does the will of your soul. A renewed mind (soul) proves the will of God and is Holy Spirit led. We don't need to convince God what His will is; we need to convince and prove it to ourselves by renewing our minds.

*"And do not be conformed to this world, but be transformed by the renewing of your mind, that you may prove what is that good and acceptable and perfect will of God." Romans 12:2*

Your body houses the results of your mind, will, and emotions. That is why it is imperative to renew your mind. The decisions you make will affect the physical part of you.

We are thinking beings. The average person has more than six thousand thoughts in a day. Every time you think a thought, you are choosing and making decisions. It can be as simple as your alarm going off in the morning. You think about getting up, and then you decide how you will respond to the alarm. You think about how tired you feel and then decide to make yourself a cup of coffee to jumpstart your day. You think I have twenty minutes to get out the door, and then you decide to get dressed, brush your teeth, and get ready. You get the picture. All-day long, we think, we choose, we act.

If thoughts of fear come to mind, you get to choose at that moment whether to partner with it or not. If you decide to agree with fear, you allow the spirit of fear to lead your soul instead of the Holy Spirit. The spirit of fear will yield very different results in your body. Likewise, if you choose to make your decisions based on what you see instead of what God says, your body will house the decision you have made about it.

You are not a victim of your body. Your body is the victim of your thoughts. If your thoughts need to change, then repent and change them. That's what renewing the mind means. We are responsible for taking control of our thought life so that we will make better decisions. Don't live as a victim. You are powerful. You have the same Spirit that raised Jesus from the dead.

To renew your mind, you must be intentional about taking thoughts captive to the obedience of Christ. Sometimes we say things as Christians because we know we should, but we don't understand what we are saying. We know it is true, but we don't know how to apply the truth to our life. My goal and hope are to teach this powerful truth to you in such a way that you will know what to do every time you hear this scripture.

*"For though we walk in the flesh, we do not war according to the flesh. For the weapons of our warfare are not carnal but mighty in God for pulling down strongholds, casting down arguments and every high thing that exalts itself against the knowledge of God, bringing every thought into captivity to the obedience of Christ, and being ready to punish all disobedience when your obedience is fulfilled." 2 Corinthians 10:3-6*

First, you need to understand that you have two thoughts. Your natural man (soul) has thoughts, and your Spirit (the mind of Christ) has thoughts. The natural man deals with the law of sin and death and the spiritual man, the law of life in Christ Jesus. When most Christians read that they must take their thoughts into captivity, they usually think they need to learn how to stop their thoughts. However, scripture doesn't say to stop every thought that exalts itself against the knowledge of God. It says to bring it into captivity to the obedience of Christ.

For many years I thought that true faith had one singular thought at all times. However, having two different thoughts at the same time does not mean that you don't have faith. For example, when we hear that we are not to doubt, it doesn't mean that you have only one thought and one thought continually, and if you happen to think any other thoughts, you are in disbelief or doubt. That is not what not doubting means. To not doubt means to invest in the right thought.

The right thoughts come from the mind of Christ. The thought you invest in will be the mind from which you choose to operate. You learned the proper order of things previously. Our soul (mind, will, and emotions) is to be led by the Holy Spirit (the mind of Christ). We are not to be double-minded, which means two different minds cannot lead us.

We are to take our natural thoughts and bring them into submission to the things of the Spirit (the mind of Christ). Peter says in *1 Peter 1:13, "Therefore gird up the loins of your mind, be sober, and rest your hope fully upon the grace that is to be brought to you at the revelation of Jesus Christ."* I love this visual picture because it immediately reminds me of Paul's teaching on the armor of God. He says that we are to gird up our loins with truth. In this scripture, Peter says that we are to gird up the loins of our minds. Gird means to fasten or secure with a belt or band. It also means to prepare for action. In ancient times, whenever men needed to do physical activity, they would take their tunic and gird their loins with a belt or sash. That made them mobile, ready to run and be physical without tripping. Truth must gird our minds. Being girded with truth will keep us from stumbling.

How do we walk in the Spirit (the mind of Christ) when the natural man's thoughts come or thoughts the enemy is trying to sow? A practical way we can do this is by walking our thoughts to the cross. That is what the process looks like when taking thoughts into captivity to the obedience of Christ. What does the obedience of Christ entail? It looks like dying on the cross, resurrecting, and sitting at the right hand of the Father.

The cross signifies the law of sin and death. It represents judgment, sin, condemnation, the curse, and separation from God. The Son of God, perfect and holy, hung on that cross marred and beaten beyond recognition as a human. He did this to free us from all bondage, to unite us to Him for all eternity, and for us to be able to live abundantly. We are forever in right standing because of this one death. We are justified. So as you walk your thoughts and all your justifications on why you don't deserve something, make sure you take them to the cross and remember what it signifies.

We can fully walk in the Spirit because our body, carnal natural man, has been crucified with Christ. That includes our carnal (natural) thinking. Now we have been made alive to Christ, born again of the Spirit, which contains the mind of Christ. Let this revelation sink in as you read this scripture.

Romans 6

"Or do you not know that as many of us as were baptized
into Christ Jesus were baptized into His death? Therefore
we were buried with Him through baptism into death,
that just as Christ was raised from the dead by the glory
of the Father, even so we also should walk in newness of
life. For if we have been united together in the likeness of
His death, certainly we also shall be in the likeness of His
resurrection, knowing this, that our old man was crucified
with Him, that the body of sin might be done away with,
that we should no longer be slaves of sin. For he who has
died has been freed from sin. Now if we died with Christ,
we believe that we shall also live with Him, knowing that
Christ, having been raised from the dead, dies no more.
Death no longer has dominion over Him. For the death
that He died, He died to sin once for all; but the life
that He lives, He lives to God. Likewise you also, reckon
yourselves to be dead indeed to sin, but alive to God in
Christ Jesus our Lord."

Wow, reading these scriptures makes me jump up and down. I've been baptized into Jesus' death. Dead and buried. The body of sin has been done away with altogether. I am united with Christ, the resurrected King, and carry the likeness of His resurrection. I walk in the newness of life. I reckon myself dead to sin, the carnal man, but am fully alive to God, born again of the Spirit in Christ Jesus.

If we are dead to the carnal man, what is holding us back? An unrenewed mind. We are held back by what we are justifying in our minds. Everyone builds a narrative in their mind of where things are going to end up. Your physical reality will play to the justifications you have built up in your mind.

For example, let's say that you started getting the sniffles. The first thought that comes is, "maybe I'm getting a cold." The second thought is, "well, I've been swamped and haven't been getting the rest I need." The third thought is, "I have eaten more sugar the last few days," and so on. The rabbit trail of thoughts has begun.

What is happening here is I am having a train of thoughts that are justifying my initial thought on why I'm probably getting a cold. Your body responds to these thoughts and justifications, and your cold gets worse. You continue to justify this thinking because you now have a full-blown cold.

When it comes to thinking about a pain-free supernatural birth, many thoughts can come to mind. The natural man's thoughts will take you through the rabbit trail of why you don't deserve to have a supernatural birth or give a million reasons why it isn't possible.

The natural man's thoughts are rooted in the flesh, and the enemy loves to use natural things to condemn us. He will remind us of our past in hopes that we will get stuck in the natural justifications we have built up in our minds. Maybe you were sexually immoral in your younger years, perhaps you've had abortions, maybe you didn't do everything right in your pregnancy, or your marriage might be going through a tough season. No matter the natural thoughts that come up and even all the justifications we make regarding them on why we don't deserve this, the truth is that we don't deserve it.

We have indeed fallen short. Come face to face with those thoughts, boldly walk them to the cross and say, thank God for Jesus! I am justified through Christ. Your right; I deserved death, judgment, sickness, painful births, and more. That person who deserved all of that is dead and buried. That body of sin has been done away with, and now I am free and fully justified. Look up at the Resurrected King and reckon yourself dead to all of that, but fully alive to God born again of the Spirit in Christ Jesus. When we walk our natural thoughts to the cross, our spiritual thoughts get elevated.

Jesus died and ultimately paid our debt. He saw all the justifications and reasons why something terrible should happen to us and why we don't deserve life and life abundant. He saw it all and decided to pay the price for you so you could be free of every justification. Now there is no condemnation in Christ Jesus. There is power in knowing what Jesus has done for you and applying it to your life and every thought. So pick up your cross and follow Jesus! It is not burdensome but the most liberating thing you can do. You have been liberated!

Paul talks about how the law cannot save us from sin in *Romans 7:14-25*. The law showed him that evil is present with him. Even though he wills to do the right thing, he saw another law in his members, warring against the law of his mind, bringing him into captivity to the law of sin and death. Then He says, "who will save me from this war coming against my mind and deliver me from this body of death?" I thank God — through Jesus Christ, our Lord!

He is saying here that we were carnal, but we are dead to that now because of Jesus. Notice where the war was waged. It waged against the mind. Before Jesus, we were powerless to this, and it was always bringing us into captivity. However, now as new creations, we can take our thoughts captive.

In other words, these thoughts will come and still try to wage war against your mind, but now we have the power to bring them into captivity because of the obedience of Christ. The battle is won. When we realize this, our members (the body) responds to the freedom bought for us. *"But if the Spirit of Him who raised Jesus from the dead dwells in you, He who raised Christ from the dead will also give life to your mortal bodies through His Spirit who dwells in you." Romans 8:11.* Our mortal bodies respond to spiritual laws and truths. The Spirit that lives in us gives life not just to our spirit but also to our physical body.

It is our responsibility to walk according to the Spirit. How do we do that? We have to set our minds on the things of the Spirit by investing in the mind of Christ. Gird the loins of your mind with truth. "For those who live according to the flesh set their minds on the things of the flesh, but those who live according to the Spirit set their minds on the things of the Spirit." We must renew our minds by bringing every thought that doesn't line up with the Word of God into captivity. Choose to walk them to the cross and let your soul come into alignment with the truth. Assure your heart before Him. Then act on it. Bring your Spirit, soul, and body into proper alignment, for your internal reality will always become your external reality.

# DECLARATIONS

Declarations are a great tool in renewing the mind. Your words carry power in both the physical and spiritual worlds. Start speaking what God says and watch the circumstances in your life shift. A declaration is a formal public announcement of the beginning of a state or condition. It is the act of making an official statement of factual information. When you choose to declare what God says, you proclaim the truth over every condition.

What are the words that are coming out of your mouth? What

comes out of our mouths should line up with what we believe in our hearts. Proverbs 23:7 says as a man thinks in his heart, so is he. Our heart represents our Spirit (the mind of Christ). It is our responsibility to take the thoughts of God that are in our hearts and renew our minds with them. Then our thoughts are God's thoughts. When we renew our mind, our soul aligns with the truth, which affects the physical part of us and the physical realm. Once we start speaking the truth continuously, we will see the effects on our lives.

God did not make it hard to find the truth. The written Word gives us easy access to the truth.

*John 8:31*
*"If you abide in my Word, you are my disciple indeed. And you shall know the truth, and the truth shall make you free."*

It is important to be aware of what we are saying and be intentional to adjust anything that we are speaking that is the opposite of what God says. Your words are prophesying your future. They are seeds that will produce a harvest.

When you sow a seed, you get tremendous multiplication. One seed produces fruit that has many seeds. The same is true when you speak the Word of God over yourself. The multiplication is exponential. *"Death and life are in the power of the tongue, and those who love it will eat its fruit"* Proverbs 18:21.

If you see a harvest in your life that you don't like, the first thing you should start guarding is your tongue. *"Whoever guards his mouth and tongue keeps his soul from troubles"* Proverbs 21: 23. Your tongue (language) reveals both good and bad mindsets. Take destructive perspectives and thoughts into captivity and start renewing your mind with God's truth. Then speak it out and act on it. If your spine is out of whack, you need an adjustment. Sometimes we need an adjustment towards the things of the Spirit. Let's partner with God by speaking His Words.

Disciples of Jesus should not be speaking both blessings and curses. In James three, it says, *"Out of the same mouth proceed blessing and cursing. My brethren, these things ought not to be so. Does a spring send forth fresh water and bitter from the same opening?"* Here are some common curses women say during pregnancy:

- I'm so tired.

- My body is very uncomfortable with this big belly.

- I get so swollen.

- I'm always so sick at the beginning of my pregnancies.

- I do not like being pregnant.

- I gain weight so quickly.

- I can't control my cravings,.

- I'm so emotional.

- Pregnancy is hard.

The negative things we can say about any given situation are limitless. Sometimes these statements fly right out of our mouths without any conscious thought about what we are saying. When we speak curses repeatedly, we are making that which we don't want our reality. That's why we must study what we have been saying and adjust everything that is a curse to a blessing.

It is time to make some new habits. It takes twenty-eight to forty days of focused activity to create a new habit. If you want to change your speech, you need to engage all five senses in this process. See the truth and speak it. When you touch your pregnant belly, speak the truth out loud so you can hear it. When your eating, speak the truth that no sickness can live in the temple of God. That includes morning sickness. The goal is to get to the place that only blessings flow out of our mouths, even unconsciously.

*"You will declare a thing, and it will be established for you; so light will shine on your ways." Job 22:28*

What you declare will be established for you! Rest in God, His promises, and renew your mind. Partner with Him and take action. Don't be conformed to the world and their thoughts and speech, but align yourself with the Kingdom. You are a carrier of heaven, and when you activate the Kingdom of heaven in your life through practical action, you bring heaven to Earth.

(Read Declaration Prayer On The Next Page)

# Declaration Prayer

Father, I choose as an act of my will to loose all fear, fear of every kind, whether known or unknown. If I've been fearful or have heard things of fear about pregnancy and labor, it's gone right now in Jesus' name. I choose to remain in God's perfect love, which casts out all fear.

I choose to stay in peace. I have peace; His name is Jesus, Wonderful Counselor, Mighty God, Everlasting Father, Prince of Peace. I don't need to attain peace; it is within me. God has good plans for me and this labor. He has good plans for my baby. God gives good and perfect gifts.

I choose to loose confusion, worry, stress, and all anxiety about my pregnancy and labor. I come to you, Jesus, to get rest. I choose to remain in rest by taking your yoke and burden upon me, which is easy and light.

I loose any spirits of infirmity, any sickness, and disease of any kind. It has no place in me. The blood of Jesus has bought me. All sickness is gone right now in the name of Jesus.

I loose all pain from my body. It has no place in me. Jesus loosed the pains of death because it was not possible that He should be held by it. Therefore, I can't be held by it either.

I bind to my soul Your life, Your love, Your presence, Your joy, Your excitement, Your expectancy, Your creativity, Your peace, freedom, grace, mercy, and the plans you have for me. I bind to my soul Your ways and Your thoughts in Jesus' name.

# Standing On His Promises

# CHAPTER 11

People laughed at me all the time when I shared what God promised. "Just you wait and see." They would project doubt and say things like, "That isn't Biblical." Or if they were not Christians, they would say, "That's not possible." Yet God's promises are eternally true regardless of belief. It wasn't always easy to ignore the doubts coming from every direction in the beginning. I would take it to God in prayer, and He would remind me of His Word. I often prayed for an unshakable boldness to stand on the promises. Then I took action by renewing my mind to the word of God, and I let go of every doubt. I refused to lean on any human understanding and instead decided to trust in the Lord with my whole heart.

When you fully trust God, you believe His promises are an emphatic yes one hundred percent of the time. Not only that, you believe that He will deliver the promise to you one hundred percent of the time. I use to have significant trust issues. I believed in the promises, but I had a hard time believing that I would receive them. The doubts would attack me on the receiving end of believing, and

I caved to them. Deep down, I was afraid of being disappointed, so I self-protected.

Telling someone with trust issues to "trust" is one of the scariest statements. *"Trust in the Lord with all your heart, and lean not on your own understanding; In all your ways acknowledge Him, and He shall direct your paths." Proverbs 3:5-6.* However, walking in this truth set me free from all my trust issues across the board. Another layer of freedom was mine for the taking!

When it comes to the promises of God, are they an emphatic yes in your life? If you are honest with yourself while taking inventory of your heart, thoughts, actions, and attitudes surrounding the promises of God, where do you stand? Do you wholeheartedly trust and believe God's Word even under dire circumstances or bad reports? Is disappointment keeping you from trusting God with all your heart? Do you think God will come through for you? If not, take the leap and trust in God wholeheartedly and believe He will come through.

All the promises of God in Jesus are Yes and in Him amen! God is faithful, and His Word is settled. Therefore, any word of God spoken to you or over you is an emphatic yes. It is not a yes today and then a maybe or a no tomorrow. God changes not.

All the promises of God are YES! Does God want to bless you? YES! Does God want you to have children? YES! Does God want you to have a supernatural pregnancy and labor? YES! Does God want you and your children to be healthy and prosperous? YES! Does God want you to have a fantastic marriage? YES! Even if there are trials along the way, God still wants you to have these things. His yes does not change based on our circumstances, feelings, or how we see things.

The goal is to realize the emphatic Yes of God in Christ and walk according to the spirit and not the flesh when it comes to standing on the promises. One way we walk according to the spirit is by having an emphatic yes to what God says. On the other hand, the flesh plans according to the flesh, which means you will flip-flop your yes to no, and you may even have a constant battle between them.

*2 Corinthians 1:17*
*"Therefore, when I was planning this, did I do it lightly? Or the things I plan, do I plan according to the flesh, that with me there should be Yes, Yes, and No, No?"*

Flesh-based decisions rely on the senses and circumstances, and those continually change. That is why your yes's, and no's change. Sometimes we can even falter over the promises of God because our yes to believing them is rooted in how we feel and what we see. The flesh is leading in this case.

# Let Your Yes Be Yes And Your No Be No

When you say yes and cling to something, you are letting go of something else. Did you know that your yes also says no? For instance, when I said yes to the love of my life, Ryan Andrews, my yes also continually says no to every other man on the planet.

If a man asks me out, my response is sorry someone else has my yes, and I choose to hold on to that yes every day. If I let go of my yes to my husband even for a moment, it is sure to bring much destruction. Emotionally, physically, and relationally. Likewise, the day you said yes to Jesus as your Lord and Savior, you said no to the old man and yes to the new creation. You said yes to life and life abundant and no to sin and death.

Your yes to Jesus says yes to what the Word of God says and no to every belief that contradicts His Word. If you flip-flop your yes and no, you won't produce good fruit. "But let your 'Yes' be 'Yes,' and your 'No,' 'No.' For whatever is more than these is from the evil one." Matthew 5:37. We are to abide in God. Abiding is what bears much fruit and gives us the desires of our heart.

*John 15:7*
*"If you abide in Me, and My words abide in you, you will ask what you desire, and it shall be done for you."*


*1 John 5:14-15*
*"And this is the confidence which we have before Him, that if we ask anything according to His will, He hears us. And if we know that He hears us in whatever we ask, we know that we have the requests which we have asked from Him."*


It is time to abide. You are not abiding if the promises of God are yes over you one day and no another. For instance, God's promise of healing is for us, but if we happen to get sideswiped by sickness, will our confession of the promise change. It shouldn't. You must make up your mind and hold fast to the promises no matter the cost. The promises of God in Christ are Yes, and in Jesus, Amen.


*2 Corinthians 1:18-20*
*"But as God is faithful, our word to you was not Yes and No. For the Son of God, Jesus Christ, who was preached among you by us, was not Yes and No, but in Him was Yes. For all the promises of God in Him are Yes, and in Him Amen, to the glory of God through us."*

# Walk According To The Spirit

Walking according to the spirit is laying hold with a firm grip all of God's promises in Christ, which are an emphatic yes and amen. The Hebrew word for amen here means "*so be it*" or "*That's right!*" The words *so be it* is precisely Mary's response to the angel who spoke to her of the promise of a pregnancy and son to be named Jesus.

She submitted herself to the word of God, accepted what He said, and settled it in her heart. Mary said, "*Behold the maidservant of the Lord! Let it be to me according to Your Word.*" Notice, it's not by Mary's efforts that this will come to pass. It is by the Word of God. She partnered with the Spirit of God, and her confession to the promise of God was an emphatic yes! Amen, so be it.

During my first pregnancy, I remember women loved to share how hard their labor was and express to me, wait, and see. However, I was so confident in the promise God spoke over me that I would always reply, "I'm sorry you experienced difficult labor, but I will not. Mine will be easy."

Most women would laugh at my response or roll their eyes and say, "You say that now, but you have no experience. You will change your tune when the day comes." I would reply, "No, I will not change my tune." "Do you seriously believe you will have easy labor?" "Yes, That's right!! And nothing is going to change my mind." I refused to let experiences change my confession, and I saw the results in all four of my births.

The promises of God are an emphatic yes, one hundred percent of the time! Not just when it feels good, sounds good, looks good, or even lines up with experiences. God's yes is forever settled. It's time to permanently settle that yes within your heart and make that be the confession of your mouth. For all the promises of God are yes and display the glory of God through us. You partnering with God's yes brings Him glory.

# I can birth fearless and pain-free! Yes, and Amen!

*Isaiah 66:7-8*
*Before she was in labor, she gave birth; Before her pain came,*
*she delivered a male child. Who has heard such a thing? Who has*
*seen such things? Shall the earth be made to give birth in one*
*day? Or shall a nation be born at once? For as soon as Zion was*
*in labor, She gave birth to her children.*

Isaiah is prophesying the birth of Jesus and then the church here. I believe Mary is the pregnant woman in this verse birthing the male child (Jesus). I believe Mary had a pain-free birth.

God compares this pregnant woman in scripture to Zion. The pregnant woman brings forth suddenly, quickly, and without pain and travail. This birth is a miraculous act of God.

Zion represents the church or the bride of Christ. As soon as the church was in labor, she gave birth to her children. Before she travailed, she brought forth. We see this happen on the day of Pentecost when many were added to the church immediately. The fruitfulness of this spiritual increase is likened to a whole nation being born at once.

*Isaiah 66:9*
*"Shall I bring to the time of birth and not cause delivery?" says*

*the Lord. "Shall I who cause delivery shut up the womb?" says*
*our God.*

Once Jesus came, His government and peace would increase, and there would be no end. God will surely accomplish this.

*Isaiah 66:10-11*
*"Rejoice with Jerusalem, and be glad with her, all you who love her,*
*all you who mourn for her; That you may feed and be satisfied with the*
*consolation of her bosom, that you may drink deeply and be delighted*
*with the abundance of her glory."*

All God's people are to share in this joy, time of deliverance, and victory. Jerusalem is the mother of us all, which does not come forth from the bondwoman but of the free (Galatians 4:26-31). We are heirs of the free woman. Jesus reconciled us all, and His peace extends to the Gentiles.

*Isaiah 66:12-13*
*For thus says the Lord:*
*"Behold, I will extend peace to her like a river and the glory of*
*the Gentiles like a flowing stream. Then you shall feed; On her*
*sides shall you be carried, and be dandled on her knees. As one*
*whom his mother comforts, So I will comfort you, And you shall*
*be comforted in Jerusalem."*

Streams and rivers of living water flow through Jesus. The newborn of God (the new creation) finds the source of full blessing in God's provision in the heavenly places.

God himself will comfort you. I love that He compares the way He comforts us to the way a mother comforts her babies. In the loving arms and presence of God, we flourish again physically and spiritually. Under God's nurturing care, we receive complete restoration.

I love Isaiah sixty-six because the imagery used for building God's Kingdom is of birth and a nurturing mother. Everything born of God coming through Jesus is likened to pain-free birth! Who has heard of such a thing? God says He will do it. When it's time, will I not deliver? The one who has put all this in motion, will I shut up the womb? So rejoice, daughter of Zion. With God, all things are possible.

*Philippians 4:13*

*I can do all things through Christ who strengthens me.*

God Is My Source

# CHAPTER 12

G od is not controlling, which is so refreshing. He gave us the freedom to make our own choices. Deuteronomy 30:19-20(NLT) says, "Today, I have given you the choice between life and death, between blessings and curses. Now I call on heaven and earth to witness the choice you make. Oh, that you would choose life so that you and your descendants might live! You can make this choice by loving the Lord your God, obeying Him, and committing yourself firmly to Him. This is the key to your life."

Being good parents, we teach our kids the way that they should go. They are individuals and will make their own choices, but we still teach them where they will lead. Why do we do this? Because we love them and want the best for our children. We want them to thrive.

God is a good Father and wants the absolute best for us. He gave us His Word to bring awareness of where our choices take us. Then the Word became flesh to testify to the truth and set us free from every bad choice, sin, and bondage and gave us His righteousness. He redeemed us.

There is a deception that is luring many believers away from the simplicity of the gospel. I've even seen it happen in childbirth circles and practices. The biggest ones today are Hypnobabies and Hypnobirthing. I hear things like, "What is the big deal? I'm a Christian, and I'm putting God at the center of it, so it's ok." My heart here is to shed light on how partnering with these practices affects us, especially since they are being embraced in many Christian circles.

# THE SOURCE OF THE BLESSING

We can't buy God's blessing by our actions. It comes through Jesus, by faith, as a gift. Abiding in Jesus produces fruitfulness. In Christ, we have already been given every spiritual blessing in heaven. The enemy gets us to be unfruitful by leading us away from Jesus being the source and doing other things to achieve the blessing; in this case, a pain-free birth.

When Jesus is not the source, it disrupts the divine order of Christ being the head. Choosing the lie that there is blessing outside of Jesus through works and methods rips you off from being fruitful and free of the curse. You are going back to an old way of doing things, through toil. You are missing the revelation of Christ in you. The enemy is still selling the same old lie; "Eat this fruit, and you will have what you desire." The problem is that the fruit he baits you with leads to death (the curse). You don't need that fruit in your life. Stay away from it. Don't take the bait. You already have the blessing that leads to life. You have everything you need. There is no striving or need to do anything else but believe.

Some of the common ways the enemy baits us in childbirth to remove Jesus as the source looks like needing to be in a daydream-like meditative state or an altered state of consciousness to receive a pain-free birth. The need to tap into your feminine energy and power and look deep within is another one. I'm not saying that we shouldn't fully embrace our womanhood and unique qualities, and divine design. But there is a difference between embracing how God designed us and tapping into our femininity as the source of strength and power. Elevating oneself above God through divine femininity or god-like qualities is idolatry. We are godly; we are not God. Everything comes through Christ. *"I can do all things through Christ who strengthens me." (Philippians 4:13)*

It may seem very subtle, which is why many don't see it as a big deal. That is what makes new-age occultic practices palatable—occult means to cover, to eclipse. It will cloud and eclipse your mind from the simplicity of the gospel.

The one behind this is satan. God created him as the anointed cherub who covers (*Ezekiel 28:14*). The original word for *covers* used to describe satan is *cakak,* which means to overshadow, screen, to cover. He was a cherub that covered the very throne of God. Scripture says that God established him and that he was perfect until iniquity was found in him. He became filled with violence within and sinned. He was cast out of heaven. Now he is bent on covering the truth and the gospel.

Paul recognized that the Galatian church somehow fell away from the simplicity of the gospel and brought the issue to the light in Galatians chapter three. *"O foolish Galatians! Who has bewitched you that you should not obey the truth, before whose eyes Jesus Christ was clearly portrayed among you as crucified?"* Other translations say, *"who has cast an evil spell on you?"* How did Paul know a spirit of witchcraft had entered into the body of Christ? What was the evidence? The evidence of witchcraft is that it obscured (*covered*) the revelation they had received of Jesus Christ crucified. Jesus was no longer their source but their works.

Paul continues to say, *"Did you receive the Spirit by works or by the hearing of faith? Are you so foolish? Having begun in the Spirit, are you now being made perfect by the flesh/law?"* The things we do in the flesh by works can not perfect us or bring the blessing, for we all fall short. The blessings only come through Christ crucified and that by faith.

Why does satan want to obscure the cross? He does not want us to possess our possessions. The death and resurrection of Jesus is the only basis for all God's provision to the redeemed. Satan also wants to conceal that the cross means his total defeat. He doesn't want us to realize and fully walk in the victory that Jesus won for us. He covers this simple truth and wants us to step out of the Spirit that receives by faith and go back into a works system. He baits well-meaning people whose hearts would never be to end up in that state. That is what makes it so deceptive.

# METHODS

Many methods say they are the answer to obtain an amazing birth. Meanwhile, they lead you astray from the gospel's simplicity. To understand these practices, let's explore how they originated.

Hypnobabies instructors have a minimum of 50 hours of hypnosis training. Hypnosis involves the transfer of control away from ourselves to another person. In essence, you are willingly yielding your body, mind, and will to this spirit instead of the Holy Spirit. You are saying I don't have control, but that is not true.

One of the fruits of the Holy Spirit is self-control. Hypnosis leads to an altered state of consciousness in which the mind is very susceptible to outside suggestion. Master hypnotherapist Gerald Kein developed Hypnobabies. It focuses on specific tactics to help with the pain. These tactics include hypnotic compounding (repetition) and other medical-grade somnambulistic (sleepwalking) hypnosis techniques. That is why you need to listen to the tracks they give you over and over again.

Hypnobirthing is very similar but primarily focuses on relieving fears through self-hypnosis. Marie Mongan is the founder of Hypnobirthing and is a clinical hypnotherapist. Her method is founded on using hypnosis to relax the body during labor for a better birth outcome. "The Hypnobirthing program, which consists of in-person classes and audio recordings for pregnant women and their partners, includes breathing exercises, visualizations, music, and positive affirmations that train women to drop into a deeply meditative, relaxed state when prompted with cues. The program culminates at childbirth when the woman channels her preparation to enter into a hyper-focused state of mind, akin to daydreaming, aiming to progress through labor peacefully, without pain medication or anesthesia." from Marie Mongan's obituary in the Washington Post.

Both of these methods originate from hypnosis and use hypnotherapy to achieve pain-free labor. Hypnosis removes God from the equation and is about self. It is false empowerment and does not have its origin in God. Seeking a supernatural power that doesn't come from God is idolatry. It carries a different spirit.

As Christians, we shouldn't yield ourselves to any other spirit than the Holy Spirit? We must not program our minds with tactics that oppose God and leave us susceptible to outside suggestions. It will mess with your mind. I do not think it is a coincidence that as soon as these practices became mainstream, America's new problem has become mental health.

Programming, which is how hypnosis works, is about control. A controlling spirit doesn't come from God. He never operates that way. The Bible is clear that He doesn't program our minds. He has given us free will. With that free will, we can choose to renew our minds. Renewing the mind is about self-discipline and self-control, which is a fruit of the spirit.

With Hynpobabies and Hypnobirthing, a pain-free birth gets achieved through works, methods, and performance. It rips you off from resting in the finished work of Christ. The process and method are glorified instead of the one that makes pain-free birth possible. God is the source, and everything we do and partake of should point to the finished work of Jesus and bring Him glory. Is a pain-free birth achieved from being in the perfect daydream meditative state (by works), or did you receive it by grace through Jesus (faith)? Don't let anything obscure the power and revelation of Christ crucified.

When God is the source, we are at rest. These new-age practices rely on the system because they aren't willing to surrender and trust God fully as their source. The mentality is I must do this and do that (program my mind with tracks)to be at peace and rest. Instead, choose to live by believing, not doing. The just shall live by faith.

# MIXING SEEDS

What about Christian Hypnobirthing? Is it ok to join the two together? I call this mixing seeds, like Paul's statement, O foolish Galatians. Who is teaching you to go back to works, striving, performing, and doing? Do you receive by believing or doing? Is the blessing through Christ or hypnosis? It can't be both. Why do you want to merge Jesus and hypnosis anyhow? Maybe that's a good question to ask yourself. Then ask God what He thinks about it. What does the Word say?

Every choice we make leads to action, and every action is a seed you are sowing. We can sow to the flesh or the Spirit. *"Do not be deceived, God is not mocked; for whatever a man sows to his flesh will of the flesh reap corruption, but he who sows to the Spirit will of the Spirit reap everlasting life." Galatians 6:7-8*

Remember that this choice is yours because God isn't controlling. He shows us in his Word what choices lead to life because He loves us and wants us to thrive. He gave us His Spirit that guides and convicts, empowering us into triumph and living a life of abundance. I want to point out that the Holy Spirit convicts us of sin, righteousness, and judgment. Guilt does not come from God. Conviction, yes, guilt, no. God never guilts us into obedience. Guilt is a form of manipulation to control us into making a particular decision. Conviction is about convincing, proving, and correcting.

The enemy comes in many forms and is sly like a fox. He lures us because he wants us to sow to the flesh. Song of Solomon says to catch the little foxes that spoil the vines before they ruin our vineyard in bloom. Beware of the foxes that want to make you unfruitful.

Sowing to the Spirit brings life, and that is the harvest we want to have. Deuteronomy 22:9 says, "You shall not sow your vineyard with different kinds of seeds, lest the yield of the seed which you have sown and the fruit of your vineyard be defiled." Are you sowing with mixed seeds? When it comes to pregnancy and childbirth, are you sowing seeds of the Kingdom and seeds of the opposite kingdom? Are you sowing seeds of grace and works and mixing them? Do not mix what is to stay separated, or you will defile your vineyard.

Verse ten continues this thought by stating, "You shall not plow with an ox and a donkey together." Paul explains this well when he said, "Do not be unequally yoked together with unbelievers. For what fellowship has righteousness with lawlessness? And what communion has light with darkness? And what accord has Christ with Belial? Or what part has a believer with an unbeliever? And what agreement does the temple of God with idols? For you are the temple of the living God. As God has said:

*2 Corinthians 6:14-17*
*"I will dwell in them and walk among them. I will be their God, and they shall be My people." Therefore, "Come out from among them and be separate, says the Lord."*

Paul is not saying we can't be around unbelievers. He is making a point that God dwells in us; therefore, our lives, choices, and actions are very different. We are set apart. We don't make the same agreements and don't partake of the same things of the world. We have taken God's yoke upon us, which is easy and light. Don't yoke yourself back to a worldly works-based way of doing things.

The same concept continues in verse eleven, *"You shall not wear a garment of different sorts, such as wool and linen mixed together."* Linen is a type of spiritual purity, and wool is a type of human self-effort that generates sweat. Jesus is the sacrificial lamb that redeemed us from a life of the self and continually falling short. We aren't meant to be clothed in part by the righteousness of Jesus and partly by our self-works. In other words, we no longer do things through self-effort and performance, but everything we do is now through the righteousness of Christ. Notice what the bride of Christ wears in these verses.

*Revelation 19:14*
*"Let us rejoice and exult and give Him the glory, for the marriage of the Lamb has come, and His bride has made herself ready; it was granted her to clothe herself with fine linen, bright*

*and pure"- for the fine linen is the righteous deeds of the saints.*
*And the angel said to me, "Write this: Blessed are those who are*
*invited to the marriage supper of the Lamb." And he said to me,*
*"These are the true words of God."*

The bride is dressed in fine linen, bright and pure. It's not mixed with anything. What does this linen represent? It is the righteous deeds of the saints. We have been made free from sin. We are dead to the law/works and now have our fruit unto holiness and the end everlasting life (*Romans 6:22*). Again, everything we do is through the righteousness of Christ. We now live by believing, not by performing. He has provided everything we need, and now we live out of the knowledge of His divine provision of all things.

*1 Peter 2:9-10*
*"But you are a chosen generation, a royal priesthood, a holy*
*nation, His own special people, that you may proclaim the praises*
*of Him who called you out of darkness into His marvelous light;*
*who once were not a people but are now the people of God."*

We are not to conform to the patterns of this world. Instead, our lifestyles should be distinguishable from unbelievers. We are set apart, sanctified, made holy, a people God possesses. Our body houses the Holy Spirit, which makes us the Temple of God. We are different from the world. We are holy, for we have been born again from incorruptible seed. Our Spirit is as righteous and holy as Jesus Himself. We aren't becoming holy; we are holy.

Worldy practices and even religion leave us with a works-based mentality, always performing to become. That opposes the gospel message, which is receiving by faith, and you are. When the Father looks at you, He says you are holy and righteous. Your holiness has nothing to do with what you have done or what you are or aren't doing; it is by the blood of Jesus and His resurrection. You are perfect and complete in your Spirit.

Your Spirit is holy and perfect when you are born again, but not your body and soul. Our old man was crucified with Christ that the body of sin might be done away with, freeing us from the slavery of sin and death. Our former identity is now and forever deprived of its power. We are now joined with Christ and yield our body to Him as one who has experienced resurrection life. We are no longer governed by law but by the grace of God. Renew your mind to this truth and walk according to the Spirit.

In John 17:16-18, Jesus says, *"They are not of the world, just as I am not of the world. Sanctify them by Your truth. Your Word is truth. As You sent Me into the world, I also have sent them into the world. And for their sakes, I sanctify Myself, that they also may be sanctified by the truth."* Jesus set Himself apart for God's purpose and modeled for us a set-apart life. We are sanctified and sent because Jesus was. The sending and the sanctifying are inseparable. We, too, should set ourselves apart for God's purposes as disciples of Jesus doing His will.

Jesus is the Word made flesh, and through His body, we have been sanctified (made holy). "*He said. 'Behold, I have come to do Your will, O God.' By that will, we have been sanctified through the offering of the body of Jesus Christ once and for all. By this one offering, He has perfected forever those who are being sanctified." Hebrews 10: 9, 10 & 14.* Our Spirit is perfect forever, but our soul and body are being sanctified. As we continue in the revelation of Christ in us, it will be evident in our soul and body. Our job is to continue in the revelation and abide in Christ.

# THE PURPOSE OF LIVING HOLY

Living holy doesn't make God love you more. Living unholy

doesn't make God love you less. God loves you because He is love. You don't lose your relationship with God based on your performance. What is the purpose of living a holy life, then? Does this mean that it doesn't matter what we do? Certainly not! Sin affects your body, mind, and soul. By not submitting your flesh to the Holy Spirit, you are willfully submitting yourself to the devil, and he uses that to come against you in your physical body and your soul.

Romans 6:15-18 explains this perfectly.
*"What then? Shall we sin because we are not under law but under grace? Certainly not! Do you not know that to whom you present yourselves slaves to obey, you are that one's slaves whom you obey, whether of sin leading to death, or of obedience leading to righteousness? But God be thanked that though you were slaves of sin, yet you obeyed from the heart that form of doctrine to which you were delivered. And having been set free from sin, you became slaves of righteousness."*

Don't give Satan an open door. He comes to steal, kill, and destroy your life. He wants to harm you. Shut that door and stop empowering him. Don't yield to him or cooperate with him in any way. If a door has been opened, all you need to do is repent turning toward God. Repentance is how you take away satan's right to dominate in your life.

Thank God that your slavery to sin has ended by the blood of Jesus. The beauty of your new situation is this: now that you are free from sin, you are free to serve a different master, God. Grace frees you to choose your own master but choose carefully. You surrender yourself to become a servant bound to the one you choose to obey. If you arent fully yielding and trusting in God, you are willfully putting yourself under another master.

Jesus understood this, and we see it displayed in His answer to satan as he is being tempted in the wilderness. As satan is showing Jesus all the kingdoms of the world and their glory, he says, "All these things I will give to You if You will fall down and worship me." Then Jesus said to him, "Away with you, Satan! For it is written, 'You shall worship the Lord your God, and Him only you shall serve.' " Satan never mentioned Jesus serving him. However, Jesus knows that you are a slave to whom you obey.

One master comes with a curse, *"For as many as are of the works of the law are under the curse Galatians 3:10."* The other master became a curse for us. Look at what kind of master Jesus is. *"Christ has redeemed us from the curse of the law, having become a curse for us (for it is written, 'Cursed is everyone who hangs on a tree'), that the blessing of Abraham might come upon the Gentiles in Christ Jesus, that we might receive the promise of the Spirit through faith." vs. 13–14.* The blessing is free from the curse and received through faith. Jesus also said to His disciples in John 15:15, *"No longer do I call you servants, for a servant, does not know what his master is doing; but I have called you friends, for all things I heard from My Father I have made known to You."*

# TAKE HEED

How do we guard ourselves against deception? Jesus said, *"Take heed that no one deceives you."* The word used for deceive is planar, which means to cause to wander or lead astray. Jesus is saying here to beware and make sure that you don't allow anyone to mislead you from the truth or cause you to wander from it. To avoid deception, we first must be able to identify the truth. How do we do that? The discourse between Jesus and Pilot sheds light on this subject.

When Pilot asks Jesus if He is a king, Jesus replies, "For this cause I was born, and for this cause I have come into the world, that I should bear witness to the truth. Everyone who is of the truth hears My voice." In other words, all who love the truth recognize that what I say is true because I bear witness to the truth. Pilate replied, "What is truth?" That begs the question that the heart of humanity ponders.

To identify truth, we must know what truth is. Scripture tells us precisely what truth is.

## JESUS IS THE TRUTH!

*Jesus said to him, "I am the way the truth and the life."*
*John 14:6*

## YOUR WORD IS TRUTH!

*"Sanctify them by Your truth. Your Word is truth."*
*John 17:17*

## THE SPIRIT IS TRUTH!

*"This is He who came by water and blood-Jesus Christ: not only by water, but by water and blood. And it is the Spirit who bears witness, because the Spirit is truth."*
*1 John 5:6*

With these three things together, you can be confident you have the truth. *"For there are three that bear witness in heaven: the Father, the Word, and the Holy Spirit; and these three are one. And there are three that bear witness on earth: the Spirit, the water, and the blood; and these three agree as one." 1 John 5: 7-8*

If you are not sure whether you should integrate a practice into your life, use this simple test: **Is it true to Jesus, is it true to the Bible, and does it have the witness of the Holy Spirit?**

Paul uses this as his litmus test when warning about deception as well in 2 Corinthians 11:3-4. *"But I fear, lest somehow, as the serpent deceived Eve by his craftiness, so your minds may be corrupted from the simplicity that is in Christ. For if he who comes preaches another Jesus whom we have not preached, or if you receive a different spirit which you have not received, or a different gospel which you have not accepted, you may well put up with it!"*

What makes new-age practices so enticing to Christians is that it speaks some truth and can sound good at first. Some even quote scripture and appear good, but is it God? We know satan can quote scripture when he encountered Jesus in the wilderness. He used scripture to bait Jesus to sin; think about that.

Another example is found in the story of Paul and a certain slave girl. She was a fortune teller and made a lot of money for her masters. She followed Paul and Silas for many days crying out, "These men are servants of the Most High God, who proclaim to us the way of salvation." What she was saying was true, but it did not come from God. God was not speaking through her. She had a spirit of divination or, in the original language, a spirit of Python.

This spirit uses truth as the bait to get you hooked to receive the lie. On the outside, it seems good. She walked around, bearing witness to them. They could have thought, wow, what a remarkable new convert testifying that we proclaim the way of salvation. However, there was a big problem. This spirit didn't bear witness to the Holy Spirit. Much annoyed, Paul turns and says to this spirit, *"I command you in the name of Jesus Christ to come out of her."* And he came out that very hour.

Not all things that carry truthful statements have the Holy Spirit. This woman had supernatural abilities to tell people's future. Supernatural means more than human capability, but not all supernatural comes from God. There are two supernatural sources;

one power source comes from God, and another comes from outside of God.

Be careful of being drawn into spiritual practices that have another spirit apart from God. Does it carry a spirit that you have not received? These spirits want to lure you from the truth and eclipse the gospel message. It is an entry point to letting go of Jesus as your source, which the enemy wants. He wants to steal your place of rest, taking you to a place of continually striving, doing, and performing. Jesus is our source of rest. He says, "Come to me, and I will give you rest." You don't need anything else. Just believe and receive!

# Restoring Hope & Faith After Disappointment

# CHAPTER 13

Disappointment becomes very enticing to partner with when you don't experience what you wanted in conception, pregnancy, and birth. It's good to process the emotions; however, you don't want to stay stuck in it. The enemies' goal is to choke out God's Word, and he will even use experiences as a means to lie to you to make that happen. The lies pour in, such as you don't have what it takes, your prayers will be left unanswered, you believed, but it didn't work, so stop believing, and so on. These lies come to challenge the Word of God. If the enemy can get you to question the truth, you become vulnerable to the lie.

I have three keys I want to share in overcoming disappointment. First, let us look at how Jesus confronts and responds to Peter's disappointment in the book of John, chapter twenty-one. What happens is a powerful and life-changing moment for him in which we can all glean. Peter thought he had failed, and I'm sure he was riddled with guilt and shame because he had denied Jesus three times before He was crucified. Before all this took place, Peter said to Jesus, "Even if I have to die with You, I will not deny you." Peter was bold and loved Jesus so much. He set his mind on following Jesus at all costs, even if it meant death. However, he denied the very one he was willing to lay his life down for in the heat of the moment. Peter wept bitterly when he realized what he had done.

I'm sure the enemy came and did a real number on him in this raw, vulnerable moment. The enemy may have whispered lies to him that he doesn't have what it takes to follow Jesus. Condemnation was probably flooding his mind, as well as maybe feeling self-pity and a load of guilt. Although his story may look different from yours, one thing is the same; he was sitting in disappointment.

Peter is fishing when Jesus comes to him. I find it interesting that this particular appearance marks the third time Jesus showed Himself to the disciples after being raised from the dead because Peter denied Jesus three times. Jesus rose from the dead on the third day turning all disappointment into triumph. Disappointment and doubt happen in the waiting, but in Jesus, we always triumph for what is impossible with man is possible with God.

At Jesus' third appearance, He asks Peter three questions. *Jesus said to Simon Peter, "Simon, son of Jonah, do you love Me more than these?" He said to Him, "Yes, Lord; You know that I love You." He said to him, "Feed my lambs." He said to him again a second time, Simon, Son of Jonah, do you love Me?" He said to Him, "Yes, Lord; You know that I love You." He said to him, "Tend My sheep." He said to him the third time, "Simon, son of Jonah, do you love Me?" Peter was grieved because He said to him the third time, "Do you love Me?" And he said to Him, "Lord, You know all things; You know that I love You." Jesus said to him, "Feed My sheep. John 21:15-17*

Take notice of the way Jesus confronts Peter. He never condemned him or even said, hey, we need to talk. Tell me what happened. How do you feel about the decision you had made at that moment? Are you sorry for what you have done? He never said, oh, you of little faith; how can I trust you now, nor did he manipulate him through his emotions. Instead, Jesus spoke life and mercy over Peter, restored him, and gave him purpose.

Jesus didn't see his failure; He saw his potential. He told Peter to tend and feed My sheep. In essence, he was saying; you've got this! I believe in you! You can't stay stuck in disappointment. I'm here to pull you up and restore purpose in you so you can move forward in all that I have called you to do. I'm still calling you.

How can Jesus be so confident in us? His confidence isn't in our flesh but His Spirit within us. *Not by might nor by power, but by My Spirit,' says the Lord of hosts. Zechariah 4:6* It is not done in our strength or power, thank God. That takes a lot of pressure off because I know in and of myself I can do nothing, but I can do all things through Him.

Since the number three is significant in this chapter, I want to give you three keys to overcoming disappointment. The first key that we learned from this story is to **let Jesus restore you and give you back your purpose**. Staying stuck in disappointment will rob you of your purpose and keep you from fulfilling your calling.

Allow Him to step into your disappointment and speak the things that only He can do. If you need to write down the disappointments and tear them up as a prophetic act, do it. Then write down the Rhema words God speaks over you. His words will give you purpose and help you to run your race well.

> *"Then the Lord answered me and said: Write the vision, and make it plain on tablets, that he may run who reads it."*
> *Habakkuk 2:2*

The second key is found in the following verses. Let's read, and then I'll explain.

> *"Most assuredly, I say to you, when you were younger, you girded yourself and walked where you wished; but when you are old, you will stretch out your hands, and another will gird you and carry you where you do not wish." This He spoke, signifying by what death he would glorify God. And when He had spoken this, He said to him, "Follow Me."*
>
> *Then Peter, turning around, saw the disciple whom Jesus loved following, who also had leaned on His breast at the supper, and said, "Lord, who is the one who betrays You?" Peter, seeing him, said to Jesus, "But Lord, what about this man?" Jesus said to him, "If I will that he remain till I come, what is that to you? You follow Me." (John 21:18-23)*

After Jesus restores Peter and gives him purpose, He says that Peter would die for Him by crucifixion. After He prophecies this, He says, "Follow Me." Immediately Peter turns around, looking at John behind him, and says, what about him? I love this because it's so real. We want to compare what God has for us to what He has for others. Jesus replies, whatever I have for him, what's that to you? You follow me.

The second key we learn from this story is to **stay in your lane**. Don't compare yourself or get distracted by someone else's purpose. Don't compare yourself to other women and their experiences. You follow God wholeheartedly in all that He has for you. Stay focused. Don't look at everyone else. You have a specific purpose that only you can fulfill. A comparison will rob you of your destiny.

The third key is to **guard your heart against the Word being stolen**. You need to understand that you have an enemy coming after the Word sown into your heart. Conflict comes because of the Word. The enemy's goal is to keep you from being fruitful because fruitfulness advances God's Kingdom and makes you a force that he can't withstand.

The parable of the sower in Matthew thirteen teaches us that we are to guard our heart against all things that try to take the Word of God out of our heart. The sower sows the seed, which is the Word and the wicked one immediately comes to steal it. He doesn't want us to multiply and take dominion, which is the blessing of the Lord over our lives from the very beginning of time.

The enemy wants you to stumble over the Word through disappointment. *"He who received the seed on stony places, this is he who hears the Word and immediately receives it with joy; yet has no root in himself, but endures only for a while. For when tribulation or persecution arises because of the Word, immediately he stumbles."* Matthew 13: 20-21

We have no root in and of ourselves. In our strength, we will fail whenever troubles come. We must be rooted and grounded in the true Vine, not just when things are good but even in the trials.

Don't let go of the Word when you don't understand. Continue to abide in it. That is how a believer handles conflict. To see our heart's desires fulfilled, the Word must remain in our heart. Abiding means to stay, never let go of, and continue. Don't allow the Word to be choked out through disappointment. Protect the Word of God over your life. Guard your heart so His joy may remain in you and that your joy may be full. Joy only remains through abiding.

## 3 Keys

Jesus restores purpose.

Stay in your own lane.

Guard your heart.

# Reclaim Your Birth

If you have found yourself upset about your previous pregnancy, birth story, or miscarriages, you mustn't skip over the three keys. Once you have dealt with the disappointment and have strengthened yourself in the Lord, it is time to pursue the enemy and recover ALL. It is time to take back your ground.

First Samuel chapter thirty contains the story of David and Ziklag. The Amalekites attacked Ziklag, burned it with fire, and took captive all of David's and his men's wives, sons, daughters, and all their possessions while they were away.

When they returned to the city and saw what had happened, they all lifted their voices and wept. They were so upset that the people spoke of stoning David, which greatly distressed him. However, he chose to strengthen himself in the Lord. He asked God if he should pursue the troops that did this. The main thing he wanted to know was that if they pursued them, would they overtake them? God answered and said, *"Pursue, for you shall surely overtake them and without fail, recover ALL."* David did recover all, and nothing of theirs was lacking.

The enemy is not kind. The kingdom of God suffers violence, and the violent take it by force. It's time to pursue the enemy, overtake him, and recover ALL that he steals from us. While writing this chapter, I came accross a prophetic word that I know is meant for us, Daughters of God! We are a mighty army arising.

## A Prophetic Word by Unknown

I can hear the sound of a great and mighty army marching on the horizon. It is an army of God's daughters coming to claim their inheritance. I can hear the ground shaking violently as their boots march in unison, sending shockwaves into the enemy's camp as they come to retrieve their territory.

They have been robbed and plundered; their wombs have been assaulted, their voices have been silenced and muzzled, their worth has been questioned-but NO MORE!

I can see their eyes burning with a fierce passion for their Beloved; they are moving in response to His call. In one hand, they carry the sword of the Spirit. In the other, they hold the Blood of the Lamb.

They are moving to the sound of the Lion of the Tribe of Judah, who is roaring behind them. They have come to redeem the devastations of many generations and rebuild the ancient ruins by the Sword of His Word and the healing of His Blood.  (Rev. 12:11)

I can hear the gates of hell shrieking at the sound of this approaching army-they cannot stop what is coming. Satan did everything in his power to overpower them, but all of his attempts were futile.

For here they come, can you hear them? God's daughters of Zion, a mighty army of beauty and strength. They are coming like a Mama bear with resolve in her eyes to protect her young, to restore the family, redeem the unborn, and retrieve the lost prodigals. They are coming to pour out the sweet fragrance of Jesus into the earth.

Here they come, warriors and nurturers, soldiers and protectors. They are fierceness and love combined.

'Now you are ready, my bride, to come with me as we climb the highest peaks together...together we will wage war in the lion's den and the leopard's lair...' Song of Songs 4:8 TPT

God Almighty declares the Word of the gospel with power, and the warring women of Zion deliver its message.  Psalm 68:11

# Aligning The Spiritual & Physical

# CHAPTER 14

K nowing how our bodies function in labor as well as learning birthing positions is helpful. It is important to study these things and grow in knowledge surrounding pregnancy and birth. Knowledge without understanding, however, is futile. True wisdom comes from God.

*"For the Lord gives wisdom; From His mouth come knowledge and understanding," Proverbs 2:6.*

*"How much better to get wisdom than gold! And to get understanding is to be chosen rather than silver," Proverbs 16:16.*

To have a pain-free supernatural birth experience, we need to partner with God every step of the way. We must mesh our knowledge with His understanding, which requires trust in Him. *"Trust in the Lord with all your heart, and lean not on your own understanding; In all your ways acknowledge Him, and He shall direct your paths." Proverbs 3:5-6*

So many times, the Holy Spirit directed me precisely what to do while laboring. For instance, He would use the knowledge I had about positions and breathe understanding to me at the right moment. He whispered His wisdom to my inner man, and I understood what to do with my body. It brought revelation that directly affected how I birthed as well as the outcome. Lean on His understanding and acknowledge it. He is directing you to have the best outcome.

# Labor Positions

The least ideal labor position is fully reclining because it works against gravity and can slow labor down. Laying on your back with legs raised causes your uterus to compress all major blood vessels. Tearing and the need for an episiotomy are more likely in this position. A semi-sitting position is also not ideal. It puts stress on your perineum, impairs your coccyx mobility, and slows labor down.

Researchers believe that movement and upright positions during labor have many benefits for both the mother and baby. As a mother of four, I can attest to this through experience. I birthed all four of my babies in an upright position, which uses gravity, which works with your contractions. Now add being fearless and fully relaxed during each contraction, and you will have a fast labor. If you do these things through Jesus and the revelation of Christ in you, you will have a birth unlike anyone has seen. Birthing in a way where heaven invades earth.

Some of the many benefits of an upright position include:

+ Allows baby to move down and into the correct position.
+ It brings on stronger contractions and can shorten labor.

✝ It gives you less pain or backache.

✝ Reduces the likelihood of using gadgets like forceps.

✝ It helps open your pelvis.

✝ It decreases the chance of problems with the baby's heart rate.

✝ Less risk of compressing the mother's aorta means there is a better oxygen supply to the baby.

✝ It leads to more positive birth experiences.

Maintaining an upright position can help angle or tilt the pelvis assisting the baby's descent. Moving around during labor helps the baby progress downward as well. The added pressure of your baby's head on your cervix can help you dilate faster. An upright position also opens your pelvis and makes it easier for you to push.

I never felt the need to push and never pushed my babies out. My babies just started coming out, and I eased them through. The contractions mixed with gravity honestly did all the pushing for me. My body did all the work. I never needed to make my body do anything. I did everything with such ease.

God created our bodies to birth with ease. In the natural realm, science has studied the body and found some interesting things. Movement during labor enhances comfort by stimulating receptors in the brain that decrease pain perception. When contractions get more substantial, endorphins are released, and pain perception decreases all the more. Ultimately, your movement in response to your contractions reduces pain and facilitates labor.

Walking and standing are great to do throughout labor. I was up on my feet and constantly moving through mine. Here are some benefits of walking and standing during labor.

# Walking

- ✝ Uses gravity.

- ✝ Contractions are often less painful.

- ✝ Reduces backache

- ✝ Faster labor.

- ✝ Encourages descent.

- ✝ Baby is well aligned in your pelvis.

# Standing

- ✝ Uses gravity.

- ✝ The Baby's head can apply even direct pressure onto the cervix, helping dilation.

- ✝ Contractions are more effective and less painful.

- ✝ It helps get oxygen to the baby.

- ✝ Helps create a pushing urge.

While I labored, I would have a shift from constantly moving/walking to getting into position. Nobody told me to do these things; I just listened to the Holy Spirit and my body. I wasn't monitored during any of my births, and I never knew how far along I was. Nobody checked me. I like a very hands-off approach to birthing. That's the way I wanted it, and that's what I had.

I talked to God throughout each labor and prayed in tongues

when it came to mind. My prayer was, "God, you are my provider; tell me what to do at each moment to birth this baby quickly, with ease, joy, and peace. I depend on you to tell me what positions to use. You know exactly what I need to do." When I felt the shift in my body, I had a knowing of precisely what to do. I knew it was the Holy Spirit, so I responded through action.

Each birth looked different. I did things like sit on the toilet, take a hot shower while hanging on top of shower doors through every contraction, leaning over bathroom sinks while surrendering to every contraction by bending my knees and going completely limp, squatting, and so on. When I was showering with my daughter's labor, I grabbed my butt with each hand and shook violently up and down the flabby muscles with every contraction. I have no idea why I did this other than that's what I heard of doing at that moment. It felt really good, and Glory was born 15 minutes after I did that. It may seem weird, but it worked!

No birth technique is perfect for every person or birth. Every birth is different, and what works for one may not work for another. That is why we want to be so in tune with the Holy Spirit's leading. He knows all things and is your provider. Your midwife or doctor isn't your only provider. God himself is your true provider. Talk to Him!

## Benefits of Certain Birthing Positions:

## Sitting on the Toilet

- ✝ Uses gravity
- ✝ Helps relax the perineum
- ✝ We naturally relax our pelvic floor

- Allows you to be in a supported squat
- Pelvis opens by 30 percent giving the baby extra space to engage with the cervix
- Keeps labor progressing smoothly

## Standing Supported Squat

- Uses gravity
- It realigns your pelvis to increase the opening up to 15 percent
- Contractions are more productive and less painful
- It helps the baby line up with the angle of your pelvis
- Movement causes changes in your pelvic joints, helping the baby through the birth canal
- Helps create a pushing urge

## Squatting

- Uses gravity
- Encourages rapid descent
- Better rotation
- Excellent for fetal circulation
- Gives good pelvic alignment
- Increases the urge to push
- Less work for pushing
- Takes pressure off of the tailbone
- Decreases the need for an episiotomy
- Expands the size of your pelvis
- Decreases the need for interventions

- Relaxes and stretches the pelvic floor muscles
- Greater increase of pressure in the pelvic cavity with minimal muscular effort
- Pelvis opens by 30 percent giving the baby extra space to engage with the cervix

## Knee - Chest

- Good for back labor
- Helps rotate baby if needed
- Good position if you are having a large baby
- Takes pressure off hemorrhoids

## Kneeling Upright (On One Knee)

- Uses gravity
- Opens your pelvis
- Relieves back labor
- Takes pressure off of the tailbone
- Decreases the need for interventions
- Decreases the need for an episiotomy
- Can catch your baby when lifting one knee after crowning

## Leaning or Kneeling Forward

- Uses gravity
- Opens your pelvis
- Can help shift the baby
- Good for back labor
- Baby is well aligned in your pelvis

+- Good for pelvic rocking

## Hands and Knees

+- Good for back labor

+- Opens pelvis

+- Uses gravity to coax baby down

+- Works well for turning a posterior baby

+- Good position if you have a cervical lip

# The Pelvic Floor

The more relaxed your pelvic floor is, the easier it will be to birth your baby. Your pelvic floor muscles run from the front of your pelvis to the back of your tailbone. Like all other muscles in the body, you can tone them. You tone the pelvic floor muscles by lifting and squeezing them. To do this, first, you need to be able to find your pelvic floor muscles.

Sit down and breathe in a relaxed way, dropping your shoulders down. Now imagine that you need to use the restroom. Breathe in, and when you breathe out, pull up and in down below as if you are trying to stop yourself from peeing. What you feel is your pelvic floor tightening.

The lower part of your belly should contract and tighten, but your upper tummy muscles should not. Hold on to that contraction as you breathe normally and hold for 6 seconds. Then slowly relax all your pelvic floor. It can take up to 10 seconds to fully relax, so you don't need to rush this stage.

This exercise tones the pelvic floor muscle and helps you

realize when you are pulling up, tightening, and relaxing. Knowing this is very important for several reasons. If you are pulling up and tightening your pelvic floor while you are laboring, you will be working against your body's natural downward motion of contractions to move the baby out, creating more pain.

The key to an easy, pain-free birth is being completely relaxed and at rest. *"Come to Me, all you who labor and are heavy laden, and I will give you rest Matthew 11:28."* When the pushing stage comes, having a relaxed pelvic floor also creates more space for the baby to come out.

If you find yourself having trouble relaxing your pelvic floor during labor, sit on the toilet. You will naturally relax all those muscles because you are used to passing something from your body into the toilet. Your brain automatically says, "relax."

# Oxytocin

Oxytocin which is known as the "love hormone," plays an essential role in birth. Oxytocin means quick birth! It is derived from two Greek words, oxus and tokus, which mean quick childbirth. Moments before a baby is born, your production of oxytocin peaks, flooding your system with the love hormone. This peak can trigger the Ferguson Reflex, also called the fetal ejection reflex, in which the baby is born easily and quickly without voluntary pushing from the mother.

The Ferguson Reflex is what I experienced with all four of my births. I never pushed my babies out; my body just did it. I never grunted or had to bear down to push. My body ejected my babies, and all I did was try to control how fast they came out. With each baby, it took two FER pushes, and they were born.

The more you stay in a place of peace, no fear, and complete surrender, the more likely you are to receive the full dose of oxytocin released by your body. Let your body do the work and ease through it all. God designed our bodies to birth quickly and through Him with ease. It is built into us. Surrender to the process and receive all the benefits. The process is temporary, but the promise is permanent.

Remember true rest and ease come from Jesus. He is the source, and He wants to yoke himself to you. Isn't that mindblowing? However, it is up to you to take His yoke upon you.

If you are not relaxing during labor, you are tensing, slowing things down, and making it harder. When in labor, do a body check, especially during contractions:

- Relax your face.
- Relax your jaw.
- Relax your neck.
- Relax your shoulders.
- Relax your back.
- Relax your abdomen.
- Relax your hips.
- Relax your butt.
- Relax your pelvic floor.
- Relax your thighs down to your toes.

Remember true rest and ease come from Jesus. He is the source, and He wants to yoke himself to you. Isn't that mindblowing? However, it is up to you to take His yoke upon you. May your trust in Him be unshakable, and your surrender to the birth process be relentless. If you are resisting, you are not surrendering. Resisting labor leads to pain, but complete surrender leads to peace and ease.

# Hormones Of Labor

Did you ever wonder what goes on in the body to initiate the birthing process? The baby communicates to the mother's uterus when it's ready to be born by sending signals. These signals come in the form of hormones. Hormones are chemical messengers the body uses to relay instructions from one area to another.

Hormones help coordinate labor by telling the mother's body when the baby is ready to be born. They make sure the smooth muscles in the uterus are working together to create contractions. They also tell the cervix to dilate and prepare the mother's body for nursing.

The chemical regulators of the birthing process include oxytocin, estrogen, progesterone, and prostaglandins. Each plays a role. During pregnancy, high levels of progesterone prevent uterine contractions while the baby is developing. The first step your body needs to initiate is the decrease of progesterone so that labor can occur.

The baby initiates this process. When the baby is fully grown, it stretches the uterus walls, placing a strain on both the baby and uterus. This strain causes the release of both corticotropin-releasing hormone (CRH) and cortisol. The rise in these hormones induces the release of chemicals that trigger a rise in estrogen levels—Estriol in particular. Estriol prepares the smooth muscle of the uterus for hormonal stimulation by increasing its sensitivity to oxytocin. It also inhibits progesterone which was preventing uterine contractions from occurring while the fetus developed.

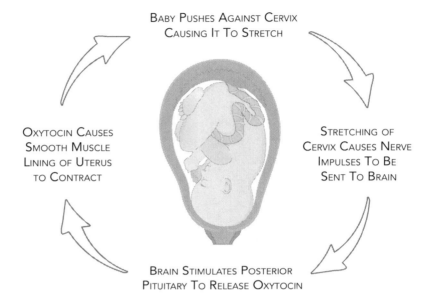

As estrogen begins to stimulate uterine contractions, the uterus produces hormones called prostaglandins, which also decrease progesterone levels helping initiate labor. Relaxin is released to relax the muscles of the cervix and create dilation. It also relaxes the muscles of the pelvis so the baby can pass through the mother's hips.

Once the uterus is primed for childbirth, the brain triggers oxytocin release from the posterior pituitary gland. Oxytocin is what keeps the uterine contractions going, and a positive feedback loop ensues. The cycle ends when the baby is born.

# Relaxin

Your pelvis is flexible, rotating, and expanding to accommodate the baby up to thirty percent. The hormone relaxin helps with this.

Relaxin is for "relaxing" your muscles, ligaments, and joints. The ovary and placenta produce it to prepare you for pregnancy and childbirth. It also softens and widens the cervix.

God designed you perfectly to expand and birth your baby without complication. Next time someone suggests that your pelvis is too small, let them know that God created the pelvis to expand and accommodate your baby.

# Coached Pushing vs. Spontaneous Pushing

I never understood when women told me they pushed for two hours until I learned more about "coached pushing." Coached pushing is when women are coached by their health care provider on when and how to push their baby.

Commonly in the USA, once fully dilated to a ten, the woman is instructed to lie on her back and immediately start pushing even if she doesn't have the urge. At the onset of a contraction, she is coached to take a deep breath and hold it while bearing down and then repeat until the baby is born. Some moms say it feels like straining to have a bowel movement.

**The Disadvantages of Coached Pushing:**

- Higher risk of tearing and severe perineal injury
- Higher rate of episiotomy

Forced pushing dismisses a woman's instinctual knowledge of when and how to push and limits her ability to give birth gently.

**Spontaneous Pushing**

Spontaneous pushing is also known as physiological or mother-led pushing. You follow your body's natural urges, pushing when you feel ready and birthing in whatever way feels suitable and most comfortable to you. Women who spontaneously push tend not to take a deep breath or hold their breath. They often exhale while pushing instead.

I spontaneously pushed for all my births. My midwives never checked me for dilation nor told me when to push. Therefore, I have no idea how long it took me to get the pushing urge after a ten dilation. The desire to push for me came with the contractions as the baby crowned. It was swift and easy. I exhaled my babies out in two FER pushes.

# Get Out of Your Thinking Brain

For labor to progress well, you need to get out of your thinking brain (neocortex) and into your primitive brain. I learned this after I birthed all of my babies, but it gave words to what I naturally did without knowing it. I followed the knowing which I call Holy Spirit unctions.

Often labor slows down because the mother is stuck in her thinking brain. For instance, she is thinking about her to-do list, if other children are being taken care of, needing to answer questions or make decisions, and so on. For me, there was always a point in labor when I knew it was time to retreat by myself, completely undisturbed, and just let go. Like I have stated before, I love to birth primarily by myself and undisturbed.

Listen to your body and cues from the Holy Spirit. You will

know when it's time to turn your thinking brain off. Have your husband help protect this time so you can relax and focus on the task at hand. It is naturally better to accomplish any job quickly when you aren't interrupted constantly. That is common sense.

# Skin to Skin Contact

One significant benefit of an unmedicated birth is that both mom and baby get a surge of hormones that help establish immediate bonding and attachment. Placing your baby skin-to-skin on your body has been scientifically proven to be one of the best things you can do! It stimulates a specific part of the newborn's brain that sends signals to the baby to move to the mom's breast, attach and begin feeding, encouraging physical development. Then the baby opens his or her eyes and gazes upon the mother, which promotes emotional and social development.

**Some of the many benefits of skin-to-skin contact are as follows:**

**For Baby:**

- Better able to absorb and digest nutrients
- Better body temperature maintenance
- Cries less often
- Demonstrate improved weight gain
- Experience more stable heartbeat and breathing
- Higher blood oxygen levels
- Long-term benefits, such as enhanced brain development and function as well as parental attachment

- More successful at breastfeeding immediately after birth
- Spend increased time in the deep sleep and quiet alert states
- Thermoregulation
- Stronger immune systems

**For Mother:**

- Experience more positive breastfeeding
- Improved breast milk production
- Likely to have reduced postpartum bleeding and lower risk of postpartum depression

Skin-to-skin contact regulates a baby's body temperature. Did you know that your breasts and abdomen can stabilize your baby's vitals and keep them warm? Mothers can naturally adjust the warmth of their breasts to keep their infant at the optimal temperature. Maternal breast temperature can rise rapidly, then fall off as the baby is warmed. As the baby starts to cool, the breasts heat up again. Isn't that amazing! God thought of everything when he fashioned woman.

Skin-to-skin contact also improves the baby's gut health and immunity. It helps the digestive system mature by stimulating the vagal nerve, causing increased growth in the villi's size providing a larger surface area for the absorption of nutrition. These babies cry less often because cortisol (stress hormone) is measurably lower after twenty minutes of skin-to-skin contact. When cortisol and somatostatin levels reduce, gastrointestinal problems decrease because it allows for better absorption and digestion of nutrients.

Another fantastic benefit is that it strengthens the baby's

immune system. There is less chance of infection because babies given skin-to-skin contact become colonized with the bacteria on their mother's skin. When that happens, it causes the mother's milk to produce antibodies in response and makes it specifically protective against those bacteria.

When you hold your baby skin-to-skin, your oxytocin levels increase, which reduces your blood pressure and stress levels. Increased oxytocin helps restore prepregnancy hormones as well.

It also helps you to produce more milk and breastfeed more successfully. Moms who have breastfeeding difficulties see improvements quickly when they start skin-to-skin care for about an hour each day.

As soon as your baby is born, have someone place your naked baby on your bare chest. Remain this way for at least an hour or more before hospital staff takes the baby away to be measured and weighed. You may need to request this in advance. Find out if this is something they practice. Let them know what you want.

# Delayed Cord Clamping

Choosing to delay clamping of the umbilical cord after birth gives your baby's health a boost. After the baby's birth, the umbilical cord is still attached from the baby's belly button to the placenta, and nutrient-rich blood remains within the umbilical cord and the placenta.

Delayed cord clamping allows extra time for the blood in the placenta and cord to flow to the baby. "They get enough iron to last them through their first year. They get white blood cells to fight infection. They get antibodies. They get stem cells to help repair their body," says Dr. Alan Greene. The benefits are worth the wait. Tell your provider you would like to delay cord clamping.

# Tips

## Pineapple

Did you know that eating pineapple during the last month of your pregnancy helps soften the cervix and get your body ready for labor? Pineapples contain bromelain, a type of proteolytic enzyme that aids in softening the cervix.

## Dates

Studies suggest that eating six dates daily during the last four weeks of pregnancy can help you have an easier, shorter labor and birth.

## Red Raspberry Leaf Tea

Drinking red raspberry leaf tea is an excellent way to tone and strengthen your uterus and pelvic area. It also aids in postpartum recovery. The recommended start is one cup a day at 32 weeks pregnant. Be sure to talk to your provider first. It is not recommended early in pregnancy because it can cause contractions.

- Faster postpartum recovery
- Improve the effectiveness of contractions
- Reduce pain during labor and after birth
- Help balance postpartum hormones

✝   Help bring in breast milk for many mothers

In the natural, every woman can do these things to increase their chances of a better birth experience. We know what the body can do, but the natural realm is limited. As a redeemed woman fully submitted to God, we have God's supernatural ability.

You can't achieve a pain-free birth through natural means. The only one who has loosed us from pain is Jesus. The only way we can do all things is through Christ, who strengthens us. How do we work the works of God? Believe in Jesus!

## Add This To Your Birth Plan

Add this to your birth plan, no negative talk. Your words aren't meaningless or powerless in your life. They carry creative power. Don't underestimate the power they have.

The words we use matter. Instead of saying things like I can't do this, say I can do all things through Christ, who gives me strength. Rather than saying I'm only dilated to 1 cm, say that's fantastic! My body is opening up and doing its job. I'm that much closer to welcoming my baby.

When it comes to a birth plan, the best thing you can do is partner with God and make your plan His plan. Co-labor with Him. His ways are perfect, His words proven, and He's the best protector creating a safe place for you to birth. What are you doing or planning on to make sure you partner with God throughout the birthing process? Seek God's voice. What is God saying to you? Hear what he is saying, then take action and advocate for yourself. Choose a care provider that supports you. Take ownership, making decisions out of peace, not fear.

# Atmosphere

You house the atmosphere for your fetus. You carry God's peace and presence. Babies feel our emotions in the womb, and they receive the hormones we release. If we release stress hormones and cortisol during pregnancy, the baby gets those stress hormones also. The stress hormones released when you worry during labor block oxytocin, slowing your labor down and increasing pain in contractions.

Make it a goal to walk through pregnancy and birth in God's perfect peace without worrying about anything. If you find yourself anxious about something, tell God about it. Then give it to Him, trusting that He is working it out for you.

*Philippians 4:6–7*
*Be anxious for nothing, but in everything by prayer and supplication, with thanksgiving, let your requests be made known to God; and the peace of God, which surpasses all understanding, will guard your hearts and minds through Christ Jesus.*

Before you birth your baby, God himself goes before you! He is with you every step of the way and thought of every detail. He will not fail you or forget you. So don't worry or be afraid about the process. Picture Him being your doula, your doctor/midwife, your provider. He's the best, and He is for you!

*Deuteronomy 31:8*
*The Lord himself will go before you. He will be with you; He will not leave (fail) you or forget (abandon; forsake) you. Don't be afraid and don't worry.*

*Psalm 23:5-6 (Voice)*
*You care for all my needs, anointing my head with soothing,*
*fragrant oil, filling my cup again and again with Your grace.*
*Certainly, Your faithful protection and loving provision will*
*pursue me where I go, always, everywhere. I will always be with*
*the Eternal, in Your house forever.*

Remind yourself that God's faithful protection and loving provision is chasing you down. It pursues you wherever you go at ALL times and in EVERY situation. It's pursuing you in every doctor appointment and check-up throughout your pregnancy, birth, postpartum, motherhood, and life.

He cares for every need you have and will provide for your every need according to His riches in Glory. Let all fear melt away as He is anointing your head with soothing, fragrant oil and filling your cup again and again with grace.

# Labor Prayer and Declarations

Abba Father, I come boldly to Your throne of grace, the throne of your gracious favor, with confidence and without fear. I refuse to be anxious. I refuse to worry about anything, but in everything, by prayer and supplication with thanksgiving and with a thankful heart, I make my requests known to you.

I thank you, Father, that my body, which you made to carry life, is perfect. When You made me, You said it is good. I lack nothing. I'm designed to carry life to full term. I was made to birth life with ease and without pain.

Thank you, Jesus, for redeeming me and setting me free from the bondage of sin, death, and the curse. Thank you, Jesus, for loosing all pain. I gladly choose You, receiving every spiritual blessing you have given to me. I bind my will to yours for heaven to come to earth through me. Your will be done on earth as it is in heaven. Your will be done in me through this birth.

I speak specifically to all the parts of my body to come into alignment with God's word and will. I have perfect peace, and all fear must go because I am God's, and He is perfect Love.

Baby, it's time to get yourself in the perfect position for birth. I command you to be head-down, facing my back, with your chin tucked to your chest and the back of your head ready to enter the pelvis. Get nice and low. The lower your head is, the more pressure on the cervix for dilation. Thank you, body and baby, for responding to the Spirit of the Most High!

Umbilical cord, I command you to be in the proper position. Cervix you will dilate fully, quickly, and without complication or pain. I declare I will have a short, easy, pain-free delivery in Jesus' name. Pain, I will not partner with you or tolerate you. Get out in Jesus' name.

Uterus, you will do what you have been designed to do perfectly. Contract and push that baby out! Pelvic floor fully relax, and pelvis open, giving the baby extra space to engage with the cervix. Thank you, Jesus, for perfect pelvic alignment!

Perineum stretch with ease and without pain or tearing. I declare this will be a pain-free supernatural birth. I receive it now and give all glory to God!

## IN JESUS' NAME, AMEN!

# Motherhood At Rest

I have more good news for you. God restored motherhood to a place of rest too! Christ has redeemed us from the curse, which includes toiling in motherhood. You have everything you need to do the work of mothering from a place of peace at rest. I pray this mindset becomes your reality.

Are you settling in motherhood by saying things like being a mother is exhausting? Raising toddlers is hard work. This is just the way it is. I'm drained. Do you worry about your childrens' behaviors or their health? Do you worry if you are a good mom and have what it takes to raise them well?

Take these kinds of thoughts captive, walk them to the cross and say yes to Jesus, for He has redeemed mothering to a place of rest, peace, joy, life, power, and love. You are a partaker of His divine nature. Does God's divine nature worry, get restless, or overwhelmed? Is their lack of any sort? Partake of His character and see the shift in your life.

# About The Author

Nissa Andrews is a speaker and author with a big heart for pregnancy, childbirth, marriage, and building strong families. She and her husband founded the non-profit Revival Family to be a resource for helping families thrive; spiritually, physically, and emotionally. Nissa has been teaching Pain-Free Childbirth for over 15 years.

Many pregnant women need this message but are not looking for it. You can create change by putting a copy of this book into their hands. Buy a book directly through Amazon, or if you would like to order bulk copies, contact us: books@dreamsurfpublishing.com.

**Get Connected at www.PainFreeChildbirth.org/links**

+ Join the Pain-Free Childbirth Group

+ Listen to the podcast: "Fearless"

+ Get coaching and additional support

Find more resources for marriage, family, men, and women at RevivalFam.com

Made in United States
Orlando, FL
07 June 2022

18572181R00117